1. Introduction

In our continuous search for better ways to present our research results, the Panzer Tracts team have selected a unique approach for presenting new coverage of the Jagdpanther - by using enhanced 1:10 scale component drawings as well as the more traditional 1:35 scale multiple views of the complete Panzer. These new, precise 'as-built' drawings were created by spending thousands of hours researching, measuring, and drawing - not by scanning copyrighted drawings or adding a multitude of imaginative details and/or faked camouflage colours.

This is the first time that 'as-built' drawings of the Jagdpanther have been created to the same exacting tolerances demanded of the original producers. This was achievable only through hard work because original detailed drawings for most of the external Jagdpanther components did not survive. It took:

- Over forty trips to public museums and private collectors in England, France, Germany, Switzerland, and the U.S.A. to precisely measure surviving Jagdpanther in detail.
- Thousands of research hours digging out the surviving original documents, photographs, and drawings.
- Over 1000 hours spent drawing with a versatile CAD program by the skilled, dedicated, and interactive efforts of the authors.

Many details go unnoticed when they are hidden in the four or five view drawings of a complete Panzer printed at 1:35 scale. Therefore, we have created additional drawings for display at 1:10 scale (where lines as close as 2mm apart can be seen). In addition, it is sometimes difficult to obtain dimensions of parts that are drawn at the angles in which they were actually mounted on a Panzer. To aid the modeller and enhance the display of details, many components and parts have been redrawn to create multiple-dimension views on flat planes.

Unfortunately, many of the drawings and reports on minor modifications did not survive. Therefore, we have developed a systematic approach to identifying when modifications were introduced into a production series. Original documents, photographs, and surviving Jagdpanther are carefully examined to identify the externally visible changes (even on the belly). It is also very important to identify (by Fgst. Nr.) exactly when a Jagdpanther in a photograph or museum was produced and then use this information to establish

the chronological ;ent in comparing musc phs to ensure that parts in museums have not been altered or replaced with postwar equipment.

All of this hard work paid off in new discoveries, such as:

- The first 50 Jagdpanther hulls had 16mm thick roof plates and most of the fixtures on the roof are different than those on the rest of the Jagdpanther with 25mm thick roof plates.
- A cast (instead of a welded) bump stop for the second swing arm on both sides.
- 'Spikes' cast onto one end of most Jagdpanther track links.
- Jagdpanther carried a EM 0.9m R rangefinder that was mounted on the three 'spikes' welded on the superstructure roof in front of the rear hatch.
- There were two Jagdpanther Ausführung - an Ausf.G1 with Panzerwanne (021 B 51201) and an Ausf.G2 with Panzerwanne (021 B 51272) in which the rear deck is longer and the superstructure rear plate is shorter and at a steeper angle,
- The modification of protecting cooling air louvres on the rear deck from being penetrated by strafing aircraft by cutting up sections of Schürzen plates was actually implemented.
- A redesigned 'squashed' armour casting (021 B 51181) for the machine-gun ball mount
- Numerous internal changes.

Surviving Jagdpanther are especially useful for measuring parts and their original locations to create these accurate drawings; however, photographs of entire surviving Jagdpanther have not been included - due to the misleading effect created by missing and damaged bits. We prefer to use the space available to provide a much more useful product. .

This accurate, detailed history of the development, production, and employment of the Jagdpanther has been based solely on the content of primary source documents written during the war by those who participated in the design, production, and employment of the Jagdpanther. Thanks to the British School of Tank Technology, correspondence between Krupp and the Waffenamt on the conceptual design of the Pz.Sfl.4d (the grandfather of the Jagdpanther) survived.

2. Development and Production

2.1 Development

Prior to embarking on the first attempt to design a Sturmgeschütz mit 8.8cm, in 1939 Krupp had already been contacted by Wa Prüf 6 to prepare conceptual designs for a full-tracked armoured self-propelled gun, known as the Pz.Sfl. mit 8.8cm Flak L/56 (Pz.Sfl.IVc). In their fiscal year report for 1940/41, Krupp recorded that:

Three Versuchsfahrzeuge Pz.Sfl.IVc are being built. It is intended to increase the gun performance by mounting an 8.8cm Flak L/71. Acceptance of this model by the army has not been concluded, because the original purpose of using this self-propelled gun as a Schartenbrecher (bunker buster) against the Maginot Line has been outdated. The armour of the Pz.Sfl.IVc is not thick enough to provide adequate protection of the crew for it to be employed in offensive combat. In part this design has been surpassed by the VK 4501 Panzers from Porsche and Henschel for which we are designing the turret as well as the future 80 to 90 ton schweren Kampfwagen with a 8.8cm Kampfwagenkanone L/71.

Note: A single Pz.Sfl.IVc was actually completed as a self-propelled anti-aircraft gun and sent to Italy for troop trials in 1944 (refer to Panzer Tracts No.12-1).

Since it had not been mentioned in the above report for fiscal year ending September 1941, preliminary discussions between Krupp and Wa Prüf 6 on the conceptual design for a heavily armoured 8.8cm Sturmgeschütz (assault gun enclosed in armour) had not occurred until the last quarter of 1941. But these preliminary discussions must have occurred in late 1941, since Krupp had already prepared conceptual drawings by early January 1942.

During a meeting at Meppen on 6 January 1942, Herrn Dorn and Wölfert from the Artillerie-Konstruktion Abteilung of Fried.Krupp A.G. presented conceptual overview drawings of a Pz.Sfl.IVc2 to Major Ventz of Wa Prüf 6. Two different conceptual designs had been prepared - one powered by a Deutz-Stern-Diesel engine and the other by a Maybach HL 90 engine. Wa Prüf 6 agreed with the overall layout of the vehicle. Krupp was to prepare a further conceptual design based on an Ausführung with the Maybach HL 90 engine, maximum weight of 30 metric tons, 80mm frontal and 40mm side armour, maximum speed of 40 km/hr, gun depression of 10°, and an optional leaf spring suspension.

At a meeting in Berlin on 21 January 1942, Wölfert presented two conceptual drawings of a Pz.Sfl.IVc2 mit 8.8cm L/71 Geschütz zur Begleitung der Infanterie (armoured self-propelled gun model IVc2 with 8.8cm gun 71 calibres long for escorting infantry) to Oberst Fichtner (Chef), Obstlt. v. Wilcke, and Oberbaurat Kniepkamp of Wa Prüf 6. Because of production reasons the Maybach HL 90 engine was preferred over the Klöckner-Deutz-Stern-Diesel engine. Production capabilities also governed the choice between a torsion bar and leaf spring suspension. The latter allowed the firing height and overall height to be 100mm lower than a torsion bar suspension.

On 2 April 1942, Oberstlt. Crohn and Major Ventz of Wa Prüf 6 inspected the wooden model of the Pz.Sfl.IVc2 mit 8.8cm K. L/71 constructed by Krupp and agreed with the overall layout. Further points to be incorporated in the detailed design were:

A. Fahrgestell (chassis)

1. Increase the ground clearance from 400 to 450mm.
2. Due to the increased height, the gun depression could be reduced to 8°.
3. Determine if available wider tracks can reduce the ground pressure while staying within the allowable width of 3140mm.
4. Periscopes or pistol ports are to be used for vision to the sides and rear.
5. The periscope for the driver must be traversable to the side.
6. Investigate the installation of a commander's cupola with periscopes and a built-in traversable ring for a Flieger-M.G.

B. Geschütz (gun)

1. The lowest possible deflector is to be designed.
2. Improve the gunner's position by relocating the traversing handwheel.
3. A redesign of the gunsight should eliminate the long slit in the roof.
4. Drop the gunsight for indirect fire.

Having been sent a copy of the contract SS 006-6488/42 dated 4Jun42 from Wa Prüf 6 for three Versuchs-Pz.Sfl. IVd, on 17 June 1942, Fried.Krupp-Grusonwerk informed Krupp that the assembly of these trial vehicles did not fit into and would greatly disturb their BW-Serie (Pz.Kpfw.IV)

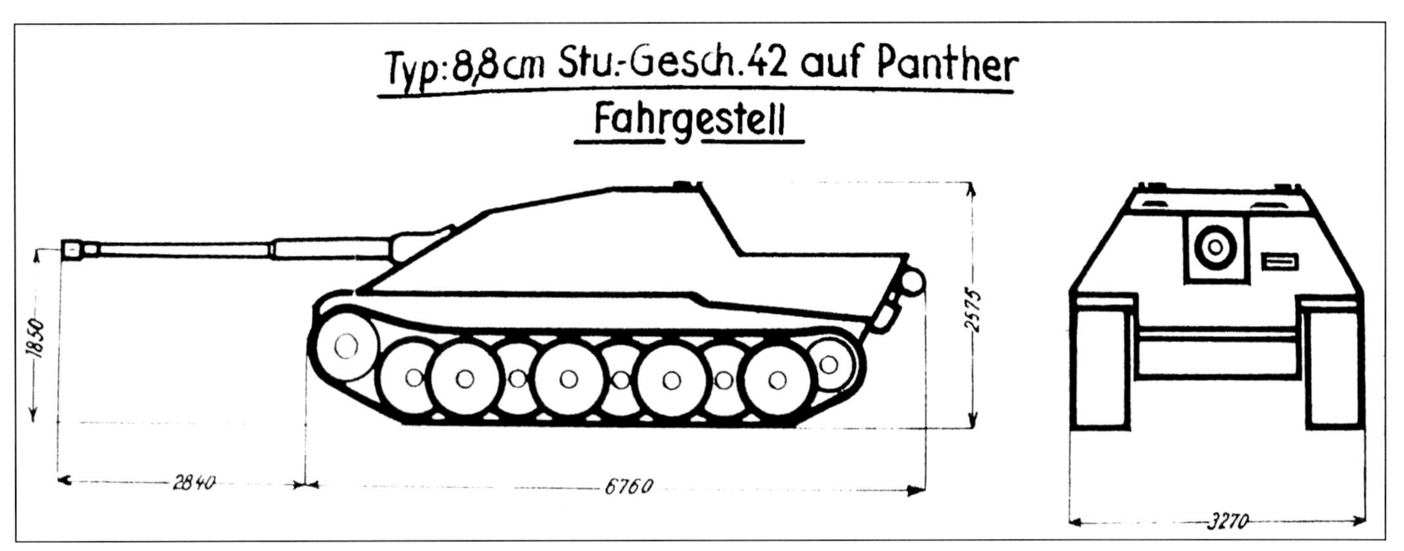

A conceptual design for the 8.8cm Stu.-Gesch.42 auf Panther Fahrgestell from 1942 when the chassis was still based on the VK 30.02(MAN) design with a submerged fording exhaust muffler. (NARA)

production program. They intended to transfer the assembly of these 3 Pz.Sfl. to Deutsche Stahlindustrie, Mühlheim. On 29 June 1942, Krupp sent contract SS 006-4735/42 dated 9Jun42 for three Versuchsaufbauten (superstructures) for Pz.Sfl.IVd back to Wa Prüf 6 with the request that this contract be given to Krupp-Grusonwerk, where the chassis were being assembled. Krupp asked Wa Prüf 6 to award the contract for production of the Panzerwanne (armour hull) and associated armour parts as Krupp proposed on 19Jun42.

A major change in design direction occurred on 3 August 1942, when Major Ventz of Wa Prüf 6 informed Krupp that the suspension and other components from the Panther were to be used for the schweren Panzerjäger (Pz.Sfl.IVd) (8.8cm L/71). Parts such as the Maybach HL 230 engines for 3 Versuchsfahrzeuge had already been ordered.

The first conceptual design drawings of the schweren Panzerjägers 8.8cm Kw.K. L/71 mit Bauelementen des Pz.Kpfw.Panther was discussed with Oberstlt. Crohn and Major Ventz from Wa Prüf 6 with Direktor Dorn and Herr Wölfert from Krupp on 9 September 1942, as follows:

1. *The unmodified Panther Fahrgestell is to be used with the engine, steering unit, transmission, entire suspension, and engine deck. The Panzerwanne could be used with minimal changes.*
2. *The 8.8cm Kw.K. L/71 is to be installed.*
3. *Wa Prüf 6 will send an example 1.5m high Sehrohr for use in observation as well as a drawing for a commander's cupola with a periscope and mount for the SF14Z scissors periscope.*
4. *Krupp is awarded a contract to complete a 1:10 scale wooden model by the end of September 1942 and a 1:1 scale wooden model by 10Nov42.*
5. *Detailed drawings were to be completed by January 1943.*
6. *Krupp is to complete 2 Versuchsfahrzeuge in armour by June 1943.*
7. *Series production was planned for delivery to start in July 1943.*
8. *Technical data included a combat weight of 35 tons with an 8.8cm Kw.K. L/71 for the main armament and an M.G.42 and two M.P. for the secondary armament. Traverse for the main gun was to be 14° to the right and 14° to the left with elevation from -8 to +14°. A total of 60 rounds of 8.8cm ammunition was to be carried. Armour protection was to consist of frontal plates of 80mm at 0° and 50mm at 60° with the side plates of 40mm at 30°. The total height of the vehicle was planned to be 2.4 metres with a firing height of 1.85 metres and a total length of 9 metres.*

Generalmajor Phillips (head of the Heereswaffenamt) stated that they intended to further develop the current Sturmgeschütz Sfl.IVd as a Panzerjäger. It was foreseen that Krupp-Grusonwerk would deliver 60 Panzerjäger each month instead of the previous plans for Panther assembly.

Presented with several conceptual design drawings of a Sturmgeschütz auf Panther during a meeting with Speer on 20-22 September 1942, Hitler ordered the production of the schweren Sturmgeschützes auf Fgst.Panther mit Panther Motor und Panther Getriebe mit der 8.8cm L71.

During a meeting at Speer's Reichsministerium für Rustung und Kriegsproduktion on 15 October 1942, it was decided that Daimler-Benz would continue design development of this vehicle, since production was to commence at the Daimler-Benz assembly plant in the Summer of 1943. Krupp was to assist Daimler-Benz with the design

A wooden model based on the conceptual design for a 8.8cm Stu.-Gesch.42 auf Panther Fahrgestell in 1942. At this time the chassis was still based on the VK 30.02(MAN) design. (NARA)

of the vehicle and still maintained primary responsibility for the design of the gun and gun mount. Even though Krupp was relieved of primary design responsibility, they were to complete a full scale-wooden model for presentation on 16 November 1942.

Herr Henze and Ebel from Daimler-Benz met with Herr Wölfert and Heerlein from Krupp A.K. on 30 October 1942 to discuss further design development of the schwerer Panzerjäger Pz.Sfl.IVd. It was decided that Krupp would complete the conceptual design up to completion of the full-scale wooden model. After the model was presented to Wa Prüf on 16 November, Daimler-Benz would take over the design work. From the available overview drawings, it was determined that the following components could be taken over from the Panther-MAN: engine, fuel system, cooling system, suspension, track drive, final drive, steering unit, and transmission. The following components would have to be newly designed or altered to fit: main drive shaft, shock absorbers, exhaust system, track tensioner, driver seat with foot petals and steering levers, shape of the hull, driver's visor, MG port and other vision devices, crew hatches, gun mount, crew compartment ventilation, gun shield, ammunition racks, and MP ports.

The full-scale wooden model of the 8.8cm Sturmgeschütz 42 (Pz.Sfl.IVd) was inspected by Oberstlt. Crohn and Ventz from Wa Prüf 6 on 24 November 1942. The following deficiencies related to the steeply angled front plate of the Sturmgeschütz were noted:

A deep box (Kugelfang - shot trap) results from mounting the gun in the steeply inclined front plate. Adding a shield to partially cover the Schacht (opening) was considered to be difficult to design and would not present an acceptable armour protection solution.

The driver's vision through the vision port is poor. Installing periscopes in the steep face results in a protrusion unfavourable for armour protection. In addition, the sight line of the driver is limited by the gun mount.

These deficiencies were to be corrected by the following proposals: The trunnions for the shield would be moved forward about 350mm. The front slope was to be interrupted by a 450mm high, 120-130mm thick wall standing at an angle of about 15°. The advantages of this layout were the elimination of the shot trap and simpler construction of the driver's vision device and openings from firing weapons for close defence. However, this would cause modification of the gun mount and installation of a counterweight. The traversing arc would be reduced by 1° and elevation also by 1° if the current firing height of 1850mm was maintained.

Due to schedule restrictions, the opening for a telescopic sight through the gun mantle was dropped. The periscopic Zieleinrichtung 37 with Sfl.ZF gunsight is to be installed. The gun mantle can again be shaped in a ball form.

Daimler-Benz was to make these changes to the full-scale model, Wa Prüf 6 is to choose the design model by 8 December 1942.

At a meeting at Daimler-Benz in Berlin-Marienfelde with Oberstlt. Ventz and Oberbaurat Rau from Wa Prüf 6 on 5 January 1943, the design of the 8.8cm Sturmgeschütz 43 (Panther) was reviewed and changed as follows:

As designed on the current proposal, the gun Scharte (embrasure) in the single piece glacis plate (55°) can only be cast and not of welded construction. Brandenburger Eisenwerke will be contracted to make a trial casting of the Scharte and gun mantle as soon as possible for quality tests and test firing. The

Scharte is to be a molybdenum-free casting 100mm thick at the rear, 60mm thick on the sides, and 40mm thick on the bottom.

Oberbaurat Rau (head of armour design and development in Wa Prüf 6) was against armour casting and expounded on the special difficulties that are to be awaited. There are shortages of alloying metals, molybdenum cannot be used, casting failures, and difficulty in heat treatment resulting in rejected castings. Unlike rolled plates with welded construction, an armour casting damaged by hits cannot be repaired. These difficulties would be significantly diminished by the sloping design of the gun mantle.

The upper front plate was to be 100mm thick and the lower front plate 60mm thick - both at an angle of 55° from the vertical. The superstructure and hull sides were to be 60mm thick. The top, bottom and rear plates were to be 30mm thick. Changes to the hull form were not necessary because M.A.N. was redesigning the steering unit.

Note: This gave the proposed Sturmgeschütz the same armour thicknesses as the hull of the proposed Panther II.

The cast Scharte was to be bolted to the front plate so that the gun carriage could be taken out the front after the Scharte was removed. If the transmission and steering unit could be removed through the hole for the gun mount, the superstructure roof was to be welded in place. An attempt was to be made to design an upright superstructure rear plate with a hatch for removing the gun tube out the rear. The lower carriage of the gun was to be modified like the model for the 8.8cm StuK 42/1 to be mounted in the Tiger P. The distance from the middle of the trunnions to the middle of the gun was 500mm instead of 430mm in the StuK 42/1. Firing height was increased to 1900mm. The gun is to be moved 30mm to the right to provide sufficient room for the driver.

Instead of a visor for the driver, two periscopes were to be mounted in the front plate, and pistol ports would provide vision to the side. A sliding plate was to cover the hole in the roof for traversing the periscopic gunsight. As requested by the troops in general a Sturmgeschütz was to be outfitted with a machinegun. Daimler-Benz was to determine if the conceptual design for a Zwillings-M.G.-Kuppel mit Scherenfernrohr (twin MG cupola with scissors periscope) could be installed for the commander.

Brandenburger Eisenwerke (Kirchmöser) was to produce all the armour components and the Sturmgeschütz was to be assembled at Daimler-Benz Werk 40 in Berlin-Marienfelde. At this time the plan was for the armour manufacturer to complete the first hulls by the mid-September 1943 and the assembly firm to complete the first production series vehicle in December 1943.

At Hitler's conference with Speer on 6 March 1943, a decision was made to examine the design of the gun mantle in the Sturmgeschütz auf Panther and, if it was possible, to use the same type of ball mount design that had been mounted in the Porsche Sturmgeschütz and the Sturmgeschütz 15cm. In all cases a gun mount design which created a shot trap as was the case with the Sturmgeschütz auf Pz.Kpfw.III was to be prevented.

A Waffenamt data sheet dated 1 May 1943 for the 8.8cm Panzerjäger 43/3 L/71 auf Panther Fahrgestell included the following details: Armour thicknesses for the superstructure were 100mm at 60° for the front, 60mm at 35° for the side, 60mm at 35° for the rear, and 30mm at 90° for the roof. The hull consisted of a glacis plate of 100mm at 55°, lower front plate of 60mm at 55°, sides at 60mm at 0°, rear of 60mm at 30°, deck of 30mm at 90°, and the belly of 30mm at 90°. In addition to the 8.8cm Pak 43/3 armament, an M.G.34 and two M.P.38s were to be carried loose inside the vehicle. Vision was to be provided by an Sfl.Z.F.5 periscopic gunsight, an S.F.14Z scissors periscope, and seven additional periscopes. A crew of five was needed consisting of the commander, gunner, driver, and two loaders. The radio sets specified were the Fu.G.15 and Fu.G.16 commonly used by the artillery. The Batterie and Abteilung commander's vehicles were also to be outfitted with a longer range Fu.G.8 radio set.

By 4 May 1943, a decision had been made to continue production of the Panther I. The Panther II design was to be shelved and not go into series production. Several modifications had been incorporated into the design of the Panther II to simplify production, and these were to be incorporated into the revised designs for the Panther I and the schwere Sturmgeschütz 8.8cm. Since the original design basis used by Daimler-Benz had been the Panther II hull, they were ordered to revise the design and base it on the Panther I chassis but incorporate the simplifying modifications of the Panther II design. These changes were to be quickly implemented in the design so that the first hulls could be delivered in September. The new armour thicknesses were to be 80mm at for the superstructure front, 50mm for the lower hull front and 50mm at 29° for the superstructure sides, and 40mm for the superstructure rear, hull sides, and hull rear. Only plate thicknesses of 16, 25, 40, 50, and 80mm were to be used.

A decision had been made by late December 1942 to have the 8.8cm Stu.-Gesch.42 auf Panther-Fahrgestell assembled at Mühlenbau und Industrie A.G. (M.I.A.G.) in Braunschweig. Responsibility for the detailed design had been passed on to M.I.A.G. from Daimler-Benz by 24 May 1943, when M.I.A.G. advised Krupp to redesign the interior travel lock. It had been previously fastened to the 30mm thick roof, but since the roof thickness had been reduced to 16mm, a travel lock holding the gun at 8° elevation should be relocated to a position below the gun supported by the hull. Since the gun had been offset 50mm to the right of the vehicle centreline to allow additional room for the driver and the gun's deflector guard hit a shock absorber at maximum elevation and traverse, M.I.A.G. proposed that the traverse arc be reduced from 14° to 12° right and 12° left. M.I.A.G. was to try relocating the shock absorber to obtain a 24° traverse arc at maximum elevation.

By 9 June 1943, the Wa Prüf 6 specification for the officially named 8.8cm Panzerjäger 43/3 (L/71) Panther with a 8.8cm Pak 43/3 (L/71) listed a crew of six (having added a radio operator), 50 rounds for the main gun, 30 rounds for a Nebelwurfgerät, 600 rounds for the M.G.42 (to engage ground targets, if possible with all-round traverse), and 760 rounds for the four M.P.40s. Instead of a direct telescopic sight for the main gun, the periscopic Sfl.Z.F.1a mit Zeileinrichtung 37 was to be mounted. The head of this periscope extended through the superstructure roof and traversed with the main gun. Vision devices were limited to two periscopes for the driver, five pistol ports (2 right, 1 left, and 2 rear), a scissors periscope S.F.14Z(Sfl.), three periscopes for the commander, and two periscopes (one traversable) for the loaders. There were only three hatches provided for the crew, one at centre right in the roof for the commander, one at the left rear in the roof above a loader, and one centred in the superstructure rear plate. In addition to the Bordsprechanlage (intercom), a mechanical device was to be added for communication between the commander and driver - either a Sprechschlauch (speaking tube) or a Maschinentelegraph as invented by Telekin. Both armour hulls for penetration tests that had been contracted from Brandenburger Eisenwerke were to be completed by 1 July 1943.

A full-scale wooden model of the mittlere Panzerjäger mit 8.8cm L/71 auf Panther, completed by Daimler-Benz, was to be transferred to M.I.A.G. by 15 June as an aid in completing assembly drawings and procedures. This same model was displayed to Hitler on 20 October 1943 along with wooden models of the Tiger II and the Jagdtiger.

Having learned the lesson at Kursk with the Ferdinand that a machinegun was needed to engage infantry and other soft targets, an M.G.34 was mounted in the superstructure front to the right of the main gun in the same ball mount introduced in the Panther. Other design modifications introduced prior to the production of the first Versuchsfahrzeug were: reduction of the crew size from six to five, an increase in the number of main gun rounds carried from 50 to 60, and a reduction in the number of vision periscopes in the superstructure roof from five to four of which two were fixed and two were traversable.

2.2 Evolution of Official Names

- **Pz.Sfl.IVc2 mit 8.8cm L/71 Geschütz zur Begleitung der Infanterie** (21Jan42 by Krupp)
- **schweren Panzerjäger (Pz.Sfl.IVd) (8.8cm L/71** (3Aug42 by Wa Prüf 6)
- **schweren Panzerjägers 8.8cm Kw.K. L/71 mit Bauelementen des Pz.Kpfw.Panther** (9Sep42 by Wa Prüf 6)
- **8.8cm Sturmgeschütz 42 (Pz.Sfl.IVd)** (24Nov42 by Wa Prüf 6)
- **8.8cm Stu.-Gesch.42 auf Panther-Fahrgestell** (Jan43 by Hauptausschuss Panzerwagen)
- **8.8cm Panzerjäger 43/3 (L/71) Panther** (1May43 by Wa Prüf 6)
- **Panzerjäger auf Fgst.Panther I** (mit 8.8cm Pak 43/3 L/71) (15Jul43 by Wa J Rue)
- **s.Panzerjäger auf auf Fgst.Panther I** (mit 8.8cm Pak 43/3 L/71) (15Sep43 by Wa J Rue)
- **Sturmgeschütz Panther für 8.8cm Stu.Kan.43 (Sd. Kfz.172)** (Oct43 by In 6)
- **Panzerjäger Panther für 8.8cm Pak 43/3 (Sd.Kfz.173** (Oct43 by In 6)
- **Jagdpanther - Suggestivname für schweren Panzerjäger auf Fahrgest.Panther** (29Nov43 by Hitler, 1Feb44 OKW, 27Feb44 OKH)
- **Panzerjäger Panther für 8.8cm Pak 43/3 (Sd.Kfz.173)** (1Mar44 in K.St.N.1149a and 1154a)
- **Jagdpanther (8.8cm Pak 43/3 L/71 auf Fgst.Panther I)** (14Mar44 by Wa J Rue)
- **s.Pz.-Jäger V 8.8cm Pak 43/3 L/71 'Jagdpanther'** (1May44 by Wa Prüf 6)
- **s.Panzerjäger mit 8.8cm Pak L/71 auf Fgst.Panther als 'Jagdpanther'** (8Sep44 by Gen.Insp.d.Pz.Tr.)
- **Jagdpanther Ausf.** [name to be used in manuals] (11Sep44 by Gen.Insp.d.Pz.Tr.)
- **Jagdpanther, Panzerjäger Panther (m. 8.8cm Pak 43/3 L/71) (Sd.Kfz.173)** (15Nov44 by Wa J Rue)
- **Jagdpanther G1** (27Feb45 by M.N.H.)

Note: It is interesting that the individual in In 6 who created the list of names in October 1943 did not recognise that the Sturmgeschütz Panther für 8.8cm Stu.Kan.43 (Sd. Kfz.172) was simply an outdated name for the Panzerjäger Panther für 8.8cm Pak 43/3 (Sd.Kfz.173).

Versuchs-Panzerjäger Panther with Fgst.Nr.V101 completed by M.I.A.G. in October 1943. (HLD)

2.3 Production

While Hitler kept demanding an increase in Panzer production, the actual monthly production goals were set by the Hauptausschuss Panzerwagen und Zugmaschinen (a committee made up of the managers of the assembly plants). Already in January 1943, plans had been laid out for the entire Programm III covering the period from April 1943 to March 1944. In this document M.I.A.G. (already designated as the assembly firm) was scheduled to deliver the first production series 8.8cm Stu.-Gesch.42 auf Panther-Fahrgestell in November 1943, followed by 5 in December, 10 in January, 15 in February, 25 in March, and 80 in July, with an end goal of increasing the rate to 150 per month.

Only two months behind the original schedule, the first five production series Jagdpanther were completed at M.I.A.G. and accepted by the Waffenamt inspectors in January 1944. Production continued at a very low rate, with seven completed in February, eight in March, 10 in April, 10 in May. These early delays in production had mainly been associated with automotive improvements in strengthening the steering units and final drive gears. Then, due to a bombing raid, production dropped to six in June 1944. Only 46 production series Jagdpanther had been completed by the end of June, compared to the production goals totalling 160 for January through June 1944. This was barely enough Jagdpanther to outfit one schwere Heeres Panzerjäger Abteilung. If the production goals had been met, there would have been a sufficient number (135) to outfit three full units plus extras for testing and training.

Production increased to 15 in July but as a result of another bombing raid had dropped off to only 14 in August. M.I.A.G. had complained about a labour shortage having caused the delays in production and were promised 300 additional workers. The Waffenamt sent 160 soldiers who started work by 4 August and an additional 160 soldiers were provided by sending 10 men from each of the 16 Panzerjäger Ersatz Abteilungen (training units). With the extra manpower, M.I.A.G. managed to complete 21 Jagdpanther in September but were again hit by a bombing raid and managed to complete only eight in October.

The causes of the production problems were related in a report dated 31 December 1944 by Dr. Blaicher (M.I.A.G.'s manager, who was also head of the Hauptauschuss Panzerwagen):

While during 1943 the influence of hostile air attacks was not yet very noticeable in the tank industry and the more important suppliers and contractors, in 1944 there was no single Panzer assembly plant which did not suffer directly and above all indirectly to a considerable extent. Insufficient supply of subcontracted parts, particularly aggravated by lengthy transport bans, must be counted as an additional difficulty for all firms during the entire year, but especially in the last four months. M.I.A.G. (Braunschweig) had to overcome the results of 10 heavy air attacks beginning in February until October 1944. The total loss of built-up area amounted to about 60%. Considerable indirect losses were caused by the continuous attacks on the city of Braunschweig. Significant additional stoppages were caused by lack of electrical power supply and absentees. The housing situation in Braunschweig today has assumed catastrophic dimensions. The population has decreased from 280,000 to 106,000. In spite of these difficulties the average monthly output amounts to 112 Sturmgeschütz and 15 Jagdpanther.

Due to the delays in production caused by bombing raids on M.I.A.G., two additional assembly plants (M.N.H. and M.B.A.) were awarded contracts to start Jagdpanther production. Maschinenfabrik Niedersachsen Hannover (M.N.H.) already had been assembling Panthers since early 1943, long before M.I.A.G. delivered 80 Jagdpanther hulls to them. As planned on 26 October 1944, M.N.H. was scheduled to complete 20 in November, 30 in December, and 30 in January and then drop out of Jagdpanther production. M.N.H. had only been selected as a stopgap firm until a new plant without any previous tank assembly experience could get past their learning curve and take over a heavy production schedule. This new firm, Maschinenfabrik Bahn Bedarf (M.B.A.), with a plant located in the suburbs of Berlin, had extensive floor space which had not been previously exploited for armoured vehicle production. The Panther-Programm dated 26 October 1944 reflected that a learning period was required by M.B.A. which was scheduled to complete the first 5 Jagdpanther in November, 10 in December, 20 in January, 30 in February, 45 in March, 60 in April, 80 in May, 90 in June and stabilised at 100 per month from July 1945.

With the contributions of both M.N.H. and M.B.A. supplementing those of M.I.A.G., 55 Jagdpanther were completed in November, 67 in December, and peak production of 72 was achieved in January 1945. M.B.A. and M.I.A.G. had not produced as many as expected, resulting in M.N.H. being scheduled to continue Jagdpanther production beyond January through June of 1945.

In his report on Panzer production dated 31 December 1944, Dr. Blaicher reported:

Two Jagdpanther completed in 1943, and 161 from January through the end of November 1944 with an additional 70 from 1 to 31 December 1944. The figures for December 1944 are not yet final. We have, however, inserted the figures which were

Versuchs-Panzerjäger Panther (Fgst.Nr. V102 completed by M.I.A.G. in November 1943) was issued to the Versuchsstelle Kummersdorf, whose vehicle number is applied in the circle painted on the glacis plate along with the Fgst.Nr. Kummersdorf were responsible for ongoing trials of new components and driving tests. Fgst.Nr. V102 had a pistol port on the left superstructure side and two on the right and was not coated with Zimmerit. Originally, this Jagdpanther had two periscopes in the front plate for the driver, but by the time this photograph was taken, the periscope on the left had been eliminated. (HLD)

Opposite and this page: One of the first production series Jagdpanther (assembled by M.I.A.G. in early 1944) still has features from the Panther Ausf.A rear deck, including an antenna base and a cap over the air intake hole in the engine deck. It also has modified Panther Ausf.A stowage bins hung from straps on the tail plate. (TTM)

One of the first eight Jagdpanther issued to schwere Panzerjäger-Abteilung 654 in late April 1944. They still had twin driver's periscopes. The tool racks on the sides were removed by the unit workshop directly before these Jagdpanther were sent to the front. (KHM)

Eight Jagdpanther, issued to the 1.Kompanie/schwere Panzerjäeger-Abteilung 654, were sent to the troop training grounds in Mailly le Camp in early August 1944. The sectional 8.8cm Pak 43/3 had started replacing the monobloc gun tubes by early April 1944. Starting in June 1944, a plate was welded over the hole for the second driver's periscope and covered by Zimmerit at the assembly plant. A single canted strip replaced the inverted V rainguard. (HLD)

stressed in discussions by the Panzer assembly firms as late as 30 December 1944. Considering the extraordinary pressure under which the Panzer assembly firms are working, particularly during the last few days, small fluctuations may yet be caused by small obstacles created by the harsh attitude of the acceptance authorities. Even the figures for December must be regarded as satisfactory if the difficulties are taken into account.

Serious examination of the deteriorating state of affairs by the Gen.Insp.d.Pz.Tr. and Waffenamt in early February led to the initiation of an emergency program calling for the limited resources still available to be concentrated on completion of the most effective armoured vehicles. On 13Feb45, the emergency production plan for Jagdpanther was:

	Feb	Mar	Apr	May	Jun
M.I.A.G	40	50	50	50	40
M.N.H	10	30	30	30	50
M.B.A	10	15	20	25	0

Due to bombing raids, electricity outages, and transportation problems only 42 Jagdpanther were completed in February, 52 in March, and about 21 in April before all three assembly plants were overrun and captured.

2.3.1 Panzerwanne Production

There was only one armour supplier contracted to weld together Panzerwanne (armour hulls) for Jagdpanther, Brandenburger Eisenwerke (Kirchmöser) in Brandenburg/Havel. As was common practice, by contract this armour manufacturer was assigned the same Wanne Nr. sequence for the armour hulls as the assembly plant was assigned for the Fgst.Nr. (chassis numbers), both series starting with 300001, the difference being that M.I.A.G. stamped the chassis number on the inside with their manufacturer's code letters 'bal' and Brandenburger Eisenwerke stamped the armour hull number on the outside with their manufacturer s code letters 'cwb'. Brandenwerke Eisenwerke completed 6 Panzerwanne by the end of October, 6 in November, 29 in December in 1943, 17 in January, 36 in February, 26 in March, 42 in April, and 38 in May for a total of 200 (already 160 ahead of M.I.A.G. assembly by the end of May 1944). They were scheduled to continue Panzerwanne production at the rate of 25 in June, 35 in July, 60 in August, 85 in September, 110 in October, 130 in November, 150 in December for a total actual and planned production of 795 Panzerwanne by the end of the 1944. The production rate was scheduled to continue at the rate of 150 per month in 1945. There is no mention in the Hauptausschuss report dated 31Dec44 of any bombing raid disrupting production at Kirchmöser in 1944, and it has been confirmed that Wanne Nr.300594 was completed in 1944. M.I.A.G. reported deliveries of 50 Jagdpanther Panzerwanne from Brandenburger Eisenwerke, Brandenburg between 28 December 1944 and 12 February 1945. The highest Wanne Nr. found to date is 300795, revealing that only about half of the armour hulls produced by Brandenburger Eisenwerke were completed as finished Jagdpanther.

Month	Planned	Accept	M.I.A.G	M.N.H	M.B.A
Oct43	1	1	1		
Nov43	5	1	1		
Dec43	5	0	0		
Jan44	15	5	5		
Feb44	15	7	7		
Mar44	15	8	8		
Apr44	30	10	10		
May44	35	10	10		
Jun44	40	6	6		
Jul44	55	15	15		
Aug44	45	14	14		
Sep44	40	21	21		
Oct44	50	8	8		
Nov44	45	55	35	20	(0)
Dec44	80	67	37	30	(0)
Jan45	90	72	35	35*	(2)
Feb45	50	42	22	(10)	(10)
Mar45	60	52	32	(10)	(10)
Apr45	60	?	3	(7)	(11)

Note: The monthly goals (planned production) are from the Wa J Rue reports in which the goals were changed monthly to reflect changed circumstances. Therefore, the planned numbers in this table do not match with the long-term planning documents.

*With the exception of 35 for December 1944, the surviving postwar report from M.N.H. does not have an exact number of Jagdpanther completed for each month but did report a total of 112 Jagdpanther. The numbers in parentheses are estimates that were calculated based on input from other primary source documents such as production goals and issue records. No reports from M.B.A. have been found, and all of their production numbers have been calculated based on subtracting both M.I.A.G. and M.N.H. from the total number reported as accepted by the Waffenamt Inspectors.

3. Changes Introduced During Production

During the production run of the Jagdpanther, modifications were introduced to improve its tactical and mechanical performance. Externally visible modifications are presented in the photos and drawings on the following pages. Production series modifications are listed by categories in the chronological order in which the changes first appeared on completed Jagdpanther leaving the assembly plants. In some cases, several months elapsed between the first appearance of a modification and the time that it was present on all new production Jagdpanther. Each assembly firm initiated changes at different times.

The assembly firms did not attempt to assemble Jagdpanther in the exact same order in which the Panzerwanne had been completed. As evidence, Jagdpanther Fgst.Nr.300099 has Wanne Nr.300185, Jagdpanther Fgst.Nr.300100 has Wanne Nr.300177, and Fgst.Nr.303018 has Wanne Nr.300294. In addition, Jagdpanther with Wanne Nr.371, 509, 597, and 605 were all being assembled at the same time by M.N.H. at the end of the war. Therefore modifications to the armour hulls, introduced sequentially by the armour manufacturer, were completely out of order on finished Jagdpanther.

A comprehensive report on modifications to the Panther Ausf.G (also applicable to the Jagdpanther Fahrgestell) published in November 1944 and a record of correspondence between M.N.H. and the Waffenamt on Jagdpanther modifications are the main sources of data. While the comprehensive report specified the official Waffenamt version of when each modification was introduced, the M.N.H. records revealed the delays that frequently occurred in actual implementation of the ordered changes. These reports were verified and expanded upon by thorough investigation of surviving Jagdpanther and photographs of Jagdpanther identified by their Fgst.Nr.

A drawing list (Gruppe Nr.51200) for the Jagdpanther also aided in identifying significant design changes when more than one number was assigned to the same component. This list was also useful in obtaining the proper designation and purpose of some components (like the spent cartridge ejection port), as follows:

51201 Panzerwanne (armour hull) *also 51271*
51211 Fussboden (floor) *also 51268*
51215 Klappe-Hülsenausstoss (spent cartridge ejection port)
51224 Munitionslagerung (ammunition racks) *also 51269*
51225 Munitionslagerung (rack for three rounds)
51226 Rohrausblasevorrichtung (fume extractor) *also 51299*
51227 Sitz-Ladeschütze (loader's seat) *also 51261*
51229 Sitz-Geschützführer (commander's seat) *also 51262*
51236 Drehplatte-Ladeschütze (loader's pivoting periscope)
51237 M.G. Kugelblende (M.G. ball mount) *also 51270*
51244 Geschütznische (cast gun recess) *also 51251*
51245 Topfblende (cast gun mantle)
51253 Einstieg (hatch)
51256 Drehplatte-Geschützführer (commander's pivoting periscope)
51277 Kampfraumheizung (crew compartment heater)
51291 Kommandantenkuppel (commander's cupola)

3.1 Track

Already at the start of the production series, all Jagdpanther left the assembly plant with Kgs 64/640/160 tracks that had six Gleitschützpickeln (raised chevrons) cast onto the face of each track link to improve traction on ice and packed snow. By July 1944, track links cast by August Engels Eisengiesserei, Werk Delligsen (code letters 'crq') had a 'spike' on the left end of each track link. Tracks with these end spikes were the normal type fitted onto most Jagdpanther.

3.2 Nahverteidigungswaffe

The three pistol ports of the superstructure sides were present on only the two Versuchsfahrzeuge Fgst.Nr.V101 and V102 and were deleted starting with the first production series Jagdpanther, Fgst.Nr.300001. These pistol port holes only weakened the base plate and were no longer necessary, since the Nahverteidigungswaffe (close defence weapon) was mounted on the superstructure roof. Due to production delays in manufacturing the Nahverteidigungswaffe, many of the Jagdpanther completed before June 1944 did not receive this weapon. When this weapon was not mounted, the hole in the superstructure roof was covered by a standardised circular plate held in place by four bolts.

3.3 Driver's Periscopes

Unlike the Versuchsfahrzeuge, at the start of the production series both periscopes were protected by a sheet metal cover that had a rubber gasket to seal the hole around the periscope.

The left driver's periscope was dropped and a 5mm thick rectangular plate was welded over the hole in the glacis plate, starting in June 1944. The design of the rain guard changed from an inverted 'V' to a single canted strip and then was dropped entirely by July 1944.

Starting in November 1944, the width of the sheet metal rain guard was increased from 206mm to 226mm on Jagdpanther with only one periscope hole.

3.4 Befehls-Jagdpanther

In addition to the Befehls-Jagdpanther for the Abteilung-Stab the Jagdpanther for the company commanders were outfitted with an Fu 8 radio set as well as the normal Fu 5 radio sets. Six out of 45 should have been completed as Befehls-Jagdpanther and therefore at least one in the first 10 by February 1944. The components for the additional radio set were mounted in the upper left superstructure rear - displacing the stowage racks for 10 rounds of 8.8cm ammunition. The antenna lead was fed through a hole in the superstructure rear plate on the left side where an armour pot was mounted to protect the porcelain insulator below the Sternantenne D. As announced in the H.T.V.Bl. in June 1944, the extension rods for the Sternantenne d were changed from 1.25m long rods with clamps to 0.7m Verlängerungsstab (extension rod) with a butterfly nut clamp. A Stützkorb (support basket), mounted on the porcelain insulator, was used to support two to six 0.7m long extension rods for increasing the height of the Sternantenne D when the Jagdpanther was stationary.

3.5 EM 0.9m R (rangefinder)

Each Jagdpanther was authorised to have an EM 0.9m R 'scissors' rangefinder that was to be used by the loader to accurately determine the range when engaging targets at long ranges. Starting in March 1944 (by Fgst.Nr.300021), three 'spikes' were welded onto the superstructure roof in front of the loader's hatch to be used for securing the mount for this EM 0.9m R.

3.6 Suspension Components

Suspension components included three different types of swing arms for the roadwheels and four different types of bump stops. The designs of these suspension components also changed during the production run.

Cast Anschlagböcke (bump stops) had replaced the welded Anschlagböcke 48393-U5 on the 1st left and right roadwheel arm stations on Jagdpanther by April 1944 when Fgst.Nr.300026 was completed by M.I.A.G.. Having parts for normal Panther, when M.N.H. started Jagdpanther assembly they installed the normal welded Anschlagböcke 48393-U5 on most of their production run. Cast Anschlagböcke were also found on Jagdpanther Fgst.Nr.303091 and 303110 completed at the end of the war.

By April 1944, two rectangular tabs had been welded to the hull sides to reinforce the Anschlagboch 48393-4 (bump stops) for the swing arms with shock absorbers, preventing them from being torn off the hull side by hard knocks. These welded tabs were dropped when Anschlagboch 48393-4 was modified to have a larger base.

M.N.H. had observed that misshapen verstärkten Siepmann-Kurbeln 48393-40 (swing arm) did not contact both Tellerfeder (disc springs) packs on a bump stop. Therefore it was decided by 13 June 1944 to again mount the rectangular shaped verstärkte Bochumer-Vereins-Kurbel 48393-14 on the 2nd left and right, 7th left, and 8th right stations, which all had shock absorbers. The verstärkte Siepmann-Kurbel 48393-40 remained on the 1st station left and right, with the normal Siepman-Kurbel 48393-30 on all the remaining stations.

Due to a shortage of Bochumer-Vereins-Kurbel 48393-14, on 13 November 1944 orders were given to install the 48393-40 (sorted out for those that were straight along the upper edge) on the 7th left and 8th right stations as well as the 1st left and right stations for the rest of the November and December 1944 production. The 48393-14 was to be mounted only on the 2nd left and right stations.

On 15 November at a meeting on modifications in Berlin, it was decided that due to a shortage of Tellerfedern, the Anschlagböcke 48393-4 were to be immediately dropped from the 7th left and 8th right stations. The four holes in the hull side were to be sealed by Kegelsenkschrauben (countersunk bolts). On 29 November 1944, Wa Prüf 6 rescinded the order to drop the rear Anschlagböcke, which were again to be mounted on the 7th and 8th stations. M.N.H. did not mount these rear bump stops on Jagdpanther with Fgst.Nr.303022 to 303025 and did mount them again starting with Fgst.Nr.303026.

A cast armour Deckel 021 B 48305 (cap) for the drive sprocket wheel hub, held by four bolts, replaced the machined cap on some Jagdpanther completed near the end of the production series in 1945.

3.7 Rear Deck

The first Jagdpanther had the same rear deck layout as a Panther Ausf.A, with the exception that narrower air intake armour louvres had been fitted directly behind the superstructure. A circular plate was bolted over the cylindrical base on the upper right rear deck since, unlike the Panther, the antenna base mount on a Jagdpanther was located on the upper right superstructure rear plate. A circular plate was also bolted over the centre hole located aft on the rear deck between the radiator and fuel filler ports. This hole had been originally intended for a telescoping tube to supply engine air while fording, but this option had been dropped before the Jagdpanther entered production. Both of these holes were no longer cut into the rear deck of Jagdpanther hulls completed after April 1944.

3.8 8.8cm Pak 43/3

The sectional 8.8cm Pak 43/3 started replacing the monobloc 8.8cm Pak 43/3 by early April 1944 (Fgst. Nr.300021). Both the sectional and monobloc guns had the same Pak 43/3 designation. The sectional gun was much easier to manufacture in two pieces than the monobloc gun, which required a single machined piece over six metres long. Other differences between the two guns were: The monobloc gun was balanced by a lead counterweight and had the breech spring operated on the right side. The sectional gun was balanced by a heavy adjustable spring and the breech spring operated on the left side. The original 5.1 litre recoil buffer was replaced by a larger 6 litre recoil buffer.

There were two different muzzle brakes, which could be fitted to either gun. The larger Mündungsbremse 05B3801-22 (originally designed for the 8.8cm Kw.K.36 and 8.8cm Pak 43/2) was 530mm long, 295mm maximum diameter, and weighed 60 kilograms. Starting in June 1944, this was replaced by a smaller Einheitsmündungsbremse M8.8 05St0816-001 (originally designed for the 8.8cm Pak 43/41) that was only 440mm long, 230mm maximum diameter, and weighed 35 kilograms.

Since guns were test fired at the gun assembly plant prior to delivery to the Jagdpanther assembly firms, a change in design was gradually implemented as stocks of the older guns were depleted, resulting in a few Jagdpanther produced as late as October 1944 still mounting the monobloc gun.

Starting in August 1944, Jagdpanther were completed with a boss cast onto the face of the Topfblende (gun mantle). A hole was drilled into the top of this boss and threaded for an eye bolt to be used for lifting the Topfblende.

3.9 Centred Anhängerkupplung (tow bracket)

An Anhängerkupplung (tow bracket) was welded to the large round Deckel (cover) for the engine access port in the hull rear (starting in May 1944 by Fgst.Nr.300042). When towing bars were attached to this centred tow bracket, vehicles with defective brakes and/or steering units or vehicles without tracks could still be stopped and controlled while being towed. Control and braking were very difficult and hazardous when towing Jagdpanther by using cables attached using C-hooks and U-shackles fitted into the holes on the hull side extensions.

3.10 Jack Mount

To make room for the tow bracket, the jack which had been mounted across the large rear engine access hatch was moved to a vertical position between the engine exhaust pipes. Holders for mounting the 20t Winden (jacks) were welded to the hull rear (starting in May 1944 by Fgst. Nr.300042).

3.11 Self-Cleaning Idler Wheel

The original idler wheel design had resulted in a build-up of encrusted mud and ice within the wheel causing, tracks to be thrown. This idler wheel was replaced with a self cleaning design starting in June 1944. The new, larger diameter idler wheel was recognizable by the double-ribbed spokes. Due to parts shortages, and in order to exhaust the supply stocks, the original design idler wheels were still mounted on several Jagdpanther completed as late as February 1945.

3.12 25mm Superstructure Roof

The first 50 Jagdpanther Panzerwanne (armour hulls) had a 16mm thick superstructure roof with the turntable exposed above the casting for the commander's rotating periscope cupola, armour guards for the periscopes at 110mm high, and commander's and loader's split hatch covers with a single external lock. Starting with Wanne Nr.300051, the roof thickness was increased to 25mm thick and the height of the cast armour base for the commander's rotating periscope cupola increased to shield the turntable. The split hatches were also redesigned with two external locks. At first the armour guards for the periscopes were still 110mm high but had been reduced to 100mm high by the Autumn of 1944. The thickness of the base plate for the loader's rotating periscope was also increased from 20 to 25mm.

3.13 Cooling Pipes

Two pipes, one mounted on each side of the right engine exhaust pipe, were added to aid in cooling the right cylinder bank and also aid in extracting fumes and smoke created by the steering units and brakes. This was accomplished by internal ductwork with air movement provided by the engine cooling fan. (First identified on Fgst.Nr.300054 completed

Above: By March 1944, unmodified Panther Ausf.A rear stowage bins were hung by straps on the tail plate. Originally, a 15-ton jack was mounted across the cover of the engine access port. (KHM)

Below: Starting in May 1944, a centred Anhängerkupplung (tow bracket) was welded to the large round engine access port in the tail plate. At the same time, the 15-ton jack was replaced by a 20-ton jack which was mounted vertically between the engine exhaust pipes. (BA)

in July 1944).

3.14 Tool and Equipment Stowage

Since they had not cut a segment out of the track guard, M.I.A.G. mounted the forward left tool stowage rack on an incline so that the bottom of the cross bar for the shovel remained above the track guard.

Initially the rear stowage bins were adopted from the Panther Ausf.A with two straps at the top over the tail plate and bottom bolted to a reinforced base plate. Starting in July 1944, the rear stowage bins were changed to the Panther Ausf.G design with straps on the back inserted into slots on the tail plate and the bottom bolted to a flat base plate. Starting in October 1944, instead of an 'X' pattern for the strengthening stripes on the face, rear stowage bins appeared with five vertical strengthening stripes on the face.

Starting in July 1944, two U-shaped brackets were welded to the top of the tail plate for retaining the rear end of the 8.2m long tow cables. Previously, the rear end of the tow cables had been retained by chains with a clip that were fastened to the bar for the spare track links.

The side track guards from M.I.A.G. were made as two segments each welded together from two pieces of sheet metal, each exactly 1380mm long. M.N.H. used the same track guards that they installed on their Panther Ausf.G with a segment cut out of the left track guard for the shovel. M.N.H. track guards were also made in two segments, but each consisted of welding together three pieces of sheet metal exactly 1000mm, 1000mm, and 760mm long.

Bent and rusted pins could not be removed from the previous threaded Schäkel (U-shackle), and there was also difficulty in getting this type produced. Conversion to Schäkel 021 D 51199-22 with Bolzen 021 E 51199-23 (pins) retained by Vorstecker 021 F 51199-24 (splints) was introduced in November 1944. When installed on the hull front, the pins were to be inserted with the heads on the outside so that the retainer would not be damaged when tracks climbed onto the drive sprocket.

At the end of the Jagdpanther production run, pipe sections with pins (for retaining the rear end of the 8.2m long tow cables) were welded to the hull sides at the rear above the bar for stowing the spare track links (replacing the U-brackets on the top of the tail plate).

3.15 Geschütznische (gun recess)

Initially, Geschütznische 021 B 51244 (gun recess) was fastened to the glacis plate by internal studs and bolts. Eight of the 80 hulls given to M.N.H. (where Jagdpanther were first competed in November 1944) were still cut for mounting the original Geschütznische 021 B 51244.

By June 1944, hulls were being completed in which a larger hole was machined out of the glacis plate with a recessed rim for seating the redesigned Geschütznische 021 B 51251. Four holes drilled into this rim at the top and four at the bottom were used for securing the Geschütznische with bolts - the bolt heads seated on flat washers being visible on the outside. Initially, starting with Jagdpanther assembled in August 1944, the casting for the Geschütznische 021 B 51251 fit exactly into the recessed rim cut into the glacis plate By October 1944, a thicker casting for Geschütznische 021 B 51251 was introduced that provided increased frontal protection from the thick lip resting on top of the glacis plate. Initially, 90mm diameter holes were drilled out of this thicker casting for countersinking the four heavy bolts at the top and bottom. Later, the lower holes were increased to 115mm diameter for better access to the bolt heads.

3.16 Zimmerit Anti-Magnetic Coating

On 7 September 1944, the Generalinspekteur der Panzertruppen decided to end the application of Zimmerit anti-magnetic coating, based on rumours that hits on the Zimmerit had caused vehicle fires. By 9 September 1944, the assembly firms had been ordered to stop applying Zimmerit anti-magnetic coating to all armoured vehicles. The assembly firms were warned that in spite of dropping this coating, the Zereissanstrich (disruptive camouflage pattern) cannot be shiny but must remain rough.

3.17 Radiator Cooling Fans

Due to the demand for improved cooling, and to strengthen the fan blades that were bent when hit, starting in September 1944, a redesigned fan was installed. Panthers with the new fan were marked with a red cross painted on the intake grill.

3.18 Final Drives Improved

In September and October 1944, a series of modifications were incorporated into the final drives as countermeasures to reported problems including chewed-up gear teeth, broken parts, damaged bearings, and insufficient lubrication.

3.19 Ball MG Armour Guard

Initially the ball machinegun mount was protected by an armour 'Gehäuse' casting in which the aperture was

The superstructure roof for the first 50 Jagdpanther hulls was 16mm thick. These first 50 can be identified by several unique features, including 110mm tall armour guards for the fixed periscopes, a 20mm thick base on the loader's traversable periscope, crew hatches with a single external lock, and the rotating plate for the commander's traversable periscope and SF14Z(Sfl.) scissors periscope was mounted higher than the cast armour base. (KHM, BA)

smooth. By October 1944, in order to reduce bullet splash, the design was changed to a stepped aperture. At the end of the production run, M.G. Gehäuse (021 B 51181) castings were introduced that had a 'squashed' profile instead of a symmetrical curve.

3.20 Elimination of Rear Shock Absorbers

The Jagdpanther's cross-country ride was almost the same with and without the rear shock absorbers. Starting in October 1944, in order to simplify production the rear shock absorbers were no longer installed at the assembly plants. M.N.H. received their order on 7 October from Wa Prüf 6 to immediately stop mounting rear shock absorbers in the Jagdpanther starting with their second Jagdpanther Fgst.Nr.303002 (completed in November 1944). Internally, the shock absorbers and arms were no longer mounted, but the Blechkasten 021 D 51104-U1 (sheet metal box) was still installed at the right rear corner of the crew compartment. The Bolzen (mounting pins) in the hull side were to be shortened to 112mm long and welded on the inside to the wall. The armour hull supplier was also informed to stop cutting a hole in the hull side for the mounting pin and an opening in the lower right corner of the firewall for the shock absorber which was expected to go into effect at the end of the year. At this time the Blechkasten 021 D 51104-U1 would also be dropped.

In practice, sometimes the hole for the shock absorber pin was closed by welding the mounting pin head on the outside of the hull or by sealing the hole with an armour plug welded to the outside of the hull (as was done on Fgst.Nr.303018).

3.21 Sockets for 2-ton Jib Boom

Starting in June 1944, a Behelfskran 2t (jib boom) was issued to the troops to aid in tank repairs. This Behelfskran was mounted on three Pilze (sockets) welded to the superstructure roof. The Behelfskran 2t could used to lift the rear decking and engine from the vehicle on which it was mounted or to lift the transmission and steering gears from an adjacent vehicle. M.I.A.G. created their own 'Pilze' design and welded one forward centre and the other two back to the right and left starting in October 1944. M.N.H. did not weld any 'Pilze' to the superstructure roof when they started Jagdpanther assembly.

3.22 Camouflage Paint Applied in Patches on Red Oxide Primer

On 31 October 1944, M.N.H. received supplementary instructions from the local Waffenamt inspector. Effective immediately, Panzerkampfwagen were no longer to be painted on the inside. The rest of the hull and components were to remain coated with red oxide primer in the condition in which they were delivered from the armour manufacturers. The outside of the Panthers was to be sparingly painted with patterns directly applied to the red oxide primer utilizing Rotbraun RAL 8017, Olivgrün RAL 6003 and Dunkelgelb RAL 7028 paste. If Dunkelgelb was not available, Dunkelgrau RAL 7021 could be used in an extreme emergency; otherwise, Dunkelgrau was to be conserved. M.N.H. requested clarification from M.I.A.G. as to whether this instruction also applied to Jagdpanther. In fact it did, as revealed by the lack of any paint except the red oxide primer on the interior of the hull and superstructure; also, about half of the exterior hull surface was left with the red oxide primer still exposed on Jagdpanther Fgst.Nr.303018 completed in late November/early December 1944.

3.23 Exhaust Pipe Heat Guards

As a temporary solution, starting late in October 1944 after Fgst.Nr.300100, sheet metal heat guards were mounted around the engine exhaust pipes in order to eliminate the glare from the red hot pipes at night.

3.24 Air Intake Vent

M.N.H. was sent 80 Panzerwannen from M.I.A.G., of which 10 with Geschütznische 021 B 51251 had the air intake vent relocated to a position at the front of the roof directly above the gun mount. These vent holes, protected by a Belüftungspilz (armour cap) on the outside, needed a new Luftschächte 021 B 51272 (ventilation duct) installed. These were not available, and authorisation was obtained to install the old Luftschächte into Fgst.Nr.303003, 006, 011, 012, 016, 017, 018, 019 and 020 (completed in November/ December 1944). The old Luftschächte was not compatible and therefore would need to be replaced if the Drageranlage (poison gas defence system) was backfitted in the future.

All other Jagdpanther before and after this period had the roof vent located on the right side of the superstructure roof directly behind the commander's hatch.

3.25 Second Driver's Periscope Hole Plugged/Deleted

The first 20 Jagdpanther delivered by M.N.H. (Fgst. Nr.303001 to 303020) still had the second driver's periscope hole covered with a 5mm thick rectangular steel plate welded to the glacis. As reported on 12 December by M.N.H., the hole was to be enlarged with a torch and the hole sealed by a welded Panzerklotz (armour plug) starting with Fgst. Nr.303021. Sometime after Wanne Nr.300186 but before Wanne Nr.300294, Jagdpanther hulls were produced with only one hole cut for the driver's periscope.

3.26 Switching Commander & Radio Operator Positions

As reported by M.N.H. on 20 December 1944, the following changes were introduced starting with the 31st Jagdpanther (Fgst.Nr.303031) that they assembled:

- The forward Munitionslagerung 021 B 41225 (ammunition stowage) for three rounds was dropped and only the Munitionslagerung 021 B 51224 was to be installed.
- The Funkanlage (radio system) and intercom box were relocated forward and the electrical cables rearranged. Since the Funkanlage was moved forward holders for an M.P., M.G. Trommeltrager, Entlader, and three Gurtsäcke were displaced to other locations.
- One of the two Sitzen 021 B 51227 (seats) for the loaders was dropped. Since the radio operator moved forward of the commander, the Sitz 021 B 51229 formerly used by the commander was now to be used by the radio operator and a new Sitz 021 B 51262 installed for the commander.

3.27 Jagdpanther Ausf.G2

While there is proof that the assembly firms did not attempt to complete Jagdpanther in a sub-series in the same order in which the Panzerwanne had been completed, photographic evidence supports the supposition that assembly firms completed each sub-series of Panzerwanne before starting on the next sub-series. It appears that all 50 Panzerwanne Nr.300001 to 300050 with 16mm roofs were completed by the assembly firm as Fgst.Nr.300001 to 300050 before starting the next sub-series with 25mm roofs. The same seems to have applied to the next sub-series with Wanne Nr.300051 to about 300300 (still with Panther Ausf.A engine compartment layout) being completed as Jagdpanther Ausf.G1 before starting to assemble Jagdpanther Ausf.G2 using Wanne Nr. starting about 300301 (with the Panther Ausf.G engine compartment layout).

3.28 Panzerwanne 021 B 51271 (Hull Armour)

A redesigned Panzerwanne 021 B 51271 (hull armour) was introduced with a lengthened rear deck and a shorter superstructure rear (to maintain the same overall length). The rear deck layout was similar but not identical to that introduced in the Panther Ausf.G. This reflected an internal change to the engine cooling system in the Jagdpanther Ausf.G2.A vent was added to the centre of the rear deck with an air scoop cowl (held by 4 bolts - not 8) covering the hole, the engine air intake covers were adapted from the Panther Ausf.G, and the rubber bumpers were dropped from the bump stops for the crew hatch. The four air intake armour louvres for the radiators were the same as those on the Panther Ausf.G. However, the filler pieces welded to the Panzerwanne behind the rear air intake louvres was wider (250mm instead of 235mm) than on a Panther Ausf.G. Two remotely operated drain plugs were added to the belly - one forward left and the other at the rear under the engine compartment.

The cooling and fume extraction pipes mounted parallel to the exhaust pipe along with the associated internal ductwork were eliminated since, due to internal changes in the engine compartment, these were no longer needed. Instead of exhaust pipes with sheet metal guards, Flammenvernichter mufflers were introduced to completely eliminate glowing exhaust pipes and to prevent engine backfiring from lighting up the Jagdpanther at night. Rounded cast armour guards to protect the openings in the hull rear for the exhaust pipes started being replaced by welded armour guards (introduced for the Panther Ausf.G in May 1944). These in turn were being replaced by castings with a 'squared-off' shape at the end of the production run.

The rear deck for Panzerwanne 021 B 51271 was designed for mounting a raised fan tower Schutzkappe 021 B 51152 (armour cover) for a Kampfraumheizung (crew compartment heater introduced in October 1944) over the left engine cooling exhaust fan. When covered by the six pie-shaped segments, air warmed by the radiators was diverted through ductwork into the crew compartment at a vent in the firewall and forward through pipes to the driver and radio operator positions. The warmed air flow could be controlled by removing individual pie-shaped segments (which were stowed on top of the Schutzkappe next to the opening). The radiator water temperature was regulated at 70 to 80°c by covering both air intakes on the right side with sliding sheet metal covers. Louvres, previously installed to regulate the engine cooling temperature, were dropped when the Kampfraumheizung was installed.

Instead of eight holes on the underside of both panniers (protected when not in use by countersunk screw plugs) on previous Jagdpanther hulls, starting with Panzerwanne 021 B 51271 there were seven short cylinders (the first position on both sides was deleted) with plugs protecting the threads when not in use. These were used to attach a hanging strap for removing roadwheels. A jack was used to raise the roadwheel to align the stud on the back of the swing arm with one of three holes on the lower end of the hanging support strap - high enough for the roadwheel to clear the track guide horns after the jack was removed.

Even the commander's, radio operator's, and loader's seats were redesigned.

3.29 Ammunition Racks

There were also numerous changes to the interior layout of the Panzerwanne 021 B 51271, including redesigned Munitionslagerung 021 B 51269 (ammunition racks). This consisted of four groups installed above the panniers on each side, with the rear groups protruding past the hull sides. Now the 8.8cm Pak 43/3 rounds in the racks on both sides at the rear were stowed with the noses pointing toward the rear.

3.30 External Tool and Equipment Stowage

To prevent loss during combat, external tool stowage was altered, with most of the tools being stowed at the rear instead of along the sides. However, the jack block mount was still welded to the right side and the cylindrical bin for the cleaning rods was still welded to the left side. Instead of mounting the convoy tail light on the left rear stowage bin, it was mounted on a bar next to the left exhaust guard, with the electrical lead feeding through an opening in the tail plate that was protected by a standard armour cap.

3.31 Ivory Paint on Superstructure Interior

On 15 February 1945, M.N.H. reported that the interior of the Wanne Jagdpanther G1 was to be again painted Elfenbein (ivory) on the inside superstructure walls and ceiling above and including the panniers. The rest of the surface was to remain unpainted (only covered with red oxide undercoat) in accordance with the Sparanstrich (paint saving) guidelines.

3.32 Gepäckkasten (stowage bin)

On 27 February 1945, M.N.H. informed the Heeres Abnahmestelle (acceptance inspector) that Gepäckkasten 021 B 51279-U12 (stowage bin) on the superstructure rear of the Jagdpanther G1 was not obtainable by them and would deliver Jagdpanther without these bins until a supply was secured. Since blocks and mounting stripes needed to be welded to the superstructure relative to the holes and contours of the Gepäckkasten, these parts could also be dropped.

3.33 Dunkelgrün base paint

As reported by M.N.H. on 15 February 1945, if the current supplies of older paint colours did not last, the new Einheitliche Farbanstrich (standardised paint coating) could be applied starting after 1 March 1945. If the older paint supplies did last, they could be applied up to 30 May 1945, but the Einheitliche Anstrich should be implemented at the latest by 1 June 1945.

3.34 Gleitschuh (skid shoe)

At the end of the production run, M.N.H. had replaced the rubber tyre return roller with a cast steel Gleitschuh (skid shoe) (found on Fgst.Nr.303091 and 303101).

Two additional modifications were introduced at the end of the production run:

- A cast Kettenrad (drive sprocket wheel) (021 B 48395-1) with a cast Deckel (cover held by 4 bolts) (021 B 48395-3).
- A redesigned Gehäuse (armour casting) (021 B 51181-4) with a 'squashed' profile for protecting the ball machinegun mount.

3.35 Modifications after Issue

The Waffenamt authorised the field units to implement a series of improvements on their Jagdpanther after issue. Among others were:

- Starting in June 1944, welding three Pilze for a Behelfskran 2t on the turret roof.
- Starting in October 1944, field units were ordered to stop applying Zimmerit anti-magnetic coating.
- Starting in December 1944, fabricating protective covers from pieces of Schürzen and installing these covers for louvres on the rear deck.
- Starting in December 1944, back-fitting Flammenvernichter mufflers.

Hauptmann Noak, commander of s.Pz.Jg.Abt.654, proposed the following modifications to the Panzerjäger Panther in a report dated 25 July 1944:

The schwere Panzerjäger Panther is a vehicle that meets all the wishes and requirements regarding mobility, armour, weapons, and outer form of a Panzerjäger. However, absolutely necessary modifications exist that are desired by the troops and which, if possible, can be incorporated into future production.

1. *Installing a traversable Kommandantenkuppel (commander's cupola) with all-round vision with the SF14Z raised through a small hatch (the same as the Sturmgeschütz auf Panzer III) - The SF14Z scissors periscope and single periscope do not provide sufficient vision for the commander and the danger exists that both will be damaged by the same hit. The commander's seat should be relocated to below his hatch and pivot through*

180°.

2. *Moving the radio equipment forward. Presently the commander has to man the hull machinegun, which distracts from his command duties. The radio operator should man the machinegun and no longer help load ammunition. Experience has proven that one loader is sufficient even in heavy firefights.*
3. *Outfitting the Befehlswagen with another Fu 2 receiver radio set. A second receiver is needed in the Befehlswagen and Chefwagen der Kompanie with Fu 8 to maintain contact with the Abteilung and attached platoons at the same time.*
4. *Modifying the Fahreroptik (driver's periscopes). The second Winkelspiegel for the driver as a substitute vision device next to the first one is unusable as mounted because the driver can neither steer nor shift gears when using this second periscope, and both get damaged by the same hit.*
5. *Adding shell fragment deflectors for the Sf.ZF (periscopic sight) and Fahreroptik.*
6. *Increasing the traverse arc of the ball-mounted machinegun.*
7. *Changing the seats - The driver's seat is too low in all vehicles and must be adjustable with a stiffer backrest. The gunner's seat must be adjustable with an improved backrest for easier access for the driver. The gunner's seat is mounted too high, and he needs a footrest.*
8. *Adding an Aussensprechanlage (speaking tube on the outside) for communication with escorted infantry.*
9. *Adding a hand brake that can be locked in position for holding the Panzerjäger in place on reverse slopes.*
10. *Adding a stop on the steering brakes.*
11. *Installing a fuel gauge.*
12. *Modifying the cooling air intake and outlet louvres on the rear deck.*
13. *Adding an additional stowage bin for crew baggage on the left superstructure rear and adding heat shields for both Gepäckkästen (stowage bins) that are already mounted on the hull rear.*
14. *Freeing the side walls of tools and equipment (relocated to the superstructure rear, rear deck, and hull rear.*
15. *Closing off the Geschütznische (gun recess) to prevent a mine or explosive charge from being shoved under the gun.*
16. *Adding a handle on the Rohrausbauluke (hatch on the superstructure rear) to make it easier and quicker to open the hatch from the outside.*
17. *Adding wing nuts on the cover for the inertial starter (hole for hand crank).*
18. *Covering various free-lying parts in the crew compartment to prevent damage.*
19. *Various. Relocate the handle on the engine hatch to the side so that the wooden block for the jack can be stowed on the rear deck. Weld a step on the last Schürze to aid in mounting. Eventually fasten the Schürzen plates with bolts to prevent their being knocked off and lost.*

Items 2, 3, 7, 14, and 16 from this list were actually acted on and modifications made to the production series (as described in the previous section). While a commander's cupola and stowage bin for the superstructure rear were designed, neither item went into production. The s.H.Pz. Jg.Abt.654 themselves modified their own Jagdpanther, implementing items 5, 13, 14, 16, and 19 above.

This Jagdpanther has the left periscope blanked off and Zimmerit applied. (KHM)

Both of these Jagdpanther with the 1. and 2.Kp./s.Pz.Jg.Abt.654, have been modified by the unit. Except for the tow cable and spare track hangers, the rest of the tool stowage has been moved to the rear. The unit also removed the second driver's periscope and plated over the hole. (KHM)

Above: Befehls-Jagdpanther from the s.Pz.Jg.Abt.559 which was captured by the Allies in September 1944. The porcelain insulator beneath the Sternantenne (star aerial) base was protected by an armour pot mounted on the superstructure rear. (NARA)
Below: Befehls-Jagdpanther (Fgst.Nr.300054 completed by M.I.A.G. in July 1944) was issued to s.Pz.Jg.Abt.559. It is shown after capture and subsequent transport to the UK for evaluation. (NARA)

Befehls-Jagdpanther (Fgst.Nr.300054) was issued to the s.Pz.Jg.Abt.559 and assigned to the commander with tactical number '01'. The rear stowage bins (the same type used by the Panther Ausf.G) are held by strips welded to the tail plate with the bottom bolted to a flat plate. Captured by the British, this Jagdpanther is currently on display in the Imperial War Museum in London. (TTM)

Above: Interior of Befehls-Jagdpanther (Fgst. Nr.300054) with a heavy counterweight bolted to the side guard on the 8.8cm Pak 43/3 gun. (TTM)

Left: In a Jagdpanther Ausf.G1 all the 8.8cm Pzgr. (AP) and Sprgr. (HE) rounds, stowed in racks above the panniers, had their noses pointed forward. Racks for the radio sets were mounted above the six rounds stowed forward on the right side above the pannier. (TTM)

The left side interior of a different Jagdpanther Ausf.G1 with the 8.8cm Pzgr. (AP) rounds stowed with the noses pointed forward. The Fernhörer (headset speakers) was stored in a box above the 18 rounds stowed above the left rear pannier. (LAC)

Ten 8.8cm Pzgr. or Sprgr. were stowed above the pannier to the left of the gunner and driver. The breech of the Nahverteidigungswaffe (close defence weapon) can be seen at the top along with the dials on the gunsight base used for setting the range when firing different types of ammunition. (LAC)

Fgst.Nr.300070 was assembled by M.I.A.G just at the point when Zimmerit anti-magnetic coating was no longer applied, as ordered on 9 September 1944. Still using the Ausf.G1 wanne, it displays the larger hole cut in the glacis plate for a larger cast Geschütznische (gun recess) secured by four external bolts at the top and bottom but still had the blanked-off driver's left periscope. The grab handles welded to the glacis plate were attached by the unit. It is shown after shipment to the US for evaluation. (USAHEC, LA)

121
ORD. OFFICER
ETOUSA
U.S. ARMY
TO COMMANDING GENERAL
ABERDEEN PROVING GROUND
BRANCH. SECT.

Some of the Jagdpanther issued to s.Pz. Jg.Abt.654 in October 1944 had the interim Geschütznische casting that exactly fit into the recessed step cut into the face of the glacis plate. (KHM)

The s.Pz.Jg.Abt.654 modified their Jagdpanther by welding a guard onto the glacis below the driver's periscope and a guard around the aperture for the gunsight periscope head. Starting in October 1944, M.I.A.G. welded three 'squat' Pilze to the roof as bases for a 2 ton Behelfskran (jib boom). (KHM)

Above: Jagdpanther (Fgst.Nr.300099 completed by M.I.A.G. in October 1944) was issued to s.Pz.Jg.Abt.654 and assigned to the 2.Kompanie. A thicker cast Geschütznische was introduced at this time which had an overlapping front to protect the recessed hole cut in the glacis plate. (KHM)

Below: Jagdpanther Ausf.G1 issued to the s.Pz.Jg.Abt.654 is rare in possessing a rear stowage bin with five vertical reinforcing stripes on its face. As a temporary solution, starting late in October 1944 after Fgst.Nr.300100, sheet metal heat guards were mounted around the engine exhaust pipes to eliminate the glare from the red-hot pipes at night. Only Jagdpanther with s.Pz.Jg.Abt.654 had stowage bins on the superstructure rear. Knocked out near Kaimig on the 18 March 1945. (NARA)

Left: Flammenvernichter mufflers have been fitted to this Jagdpanther Ausf.G1 which still has an engine compartment based on the Panther Ausf.A necessitating the need for the twin cooling pipes for the left engine cylinder bank. (LAC)

Below: This Jagdpanther completed by M.I.A.G. has the ventilation hole with armour cap on the roof relocated to a forward position above the gun. Other features unique to M.I.A.G. were the 'stubby' Pilze on the roof for the Behelfskran and the lack of a cut-out for the shovel in the left track guard. (KHM)

Above: Jagdpanther (Fgst.Nr.303018 completed by M.N.H. in December 1944) also had the ventilation hole with armour cap at the front of the roof. It does not have 'Pilze' on the roof, has a slot cut out of the left track guard for the shovel head, the loader's and commander's hatch lids are reversed with the external locks on the left, and a single hole cut in the glacis for a driver's periscope. (APG)
Below: A M.I.A.G. assembled Befehlswagen photographed in Duisberg in 1945. (SAL)

Left: A Jagdpanther Ausf.G2 with Wanne Nr.300795, the highest number identified for an armour hull welded together by Brandenburger Eisenwerke, Kirchmöser. This Jagdpanther is fitted with the new cast Kettenrad and Deckel (heavy drive sprocket with the cast hub). (LAC)

This photograph represents one of the best views of the final rare modification introduced on the Jagdpanther. The new schweres gegossenes und verstärktes Antriebskettenrad mit Radkappe (021 St 48395) (heavy cast and strengthened drive sprocket with the cast hubcap) that was expected to accompany an improved drive train with planetary gear. The Versuchsstelle Kummersdorf evaluated this heavy drive sprocket on their Bergepanther test vehicle, a photo of which can be seen in Panzer Tracts No.16-1 Bergepanther. This modification had yet to be introduced by M.N.H. when their factory in Hannover was overrun on 9 April 1945. (LAC)

Jagdpanther (Fgst.Nr.303086 completed by M.N.H. in February 1945) was captured in the Ruhr pocket area and taken to England, where it was eventually used as a target on the Pirbright ranges. The Weald Foundation acquired this Jagdpanther as a wreck in 2000. Assisted by research by the Panzer Tracts team over the following years, it was meticulously restored in every detail to a running example. All interior fittings and an original Maybach HL 230 engine are complete. (Weald Foundation)

Above: Unused Jagdpanther Ausf.G2 Panzerwanne abandoned at M.I.A.G. along with Sturmgeschütz Panzerwanne and Aufbau. A Geschütznische is resting in a few of the Jagdpanther Panzerwanne. (NARA)

Below: Partially completed Jagdpanther Ausf.G2 abandoned in the assembly hall at M.N.H. after capture by the Allies in April 1945 had Panzerwanne Nr. from as low as 300371 to as high as 300597, revealing that there was no attempt to complete Jagdpanther in the same numerical order as the hulls. (TTM)

Above: Following driving trials, this incomplete Jagdpanther Ausf.G2 was in the turret and gun fitting hall of M.N.H awaiting installation of its 8.8cm gun. However, bombing had collapsed the cranes needed to complete the assembly. (NARA)
Below: The rear deck of Jagdpanther Ausf.G2 (Fgst.Nr.303094 completed by M.N.H. in February 1945) has features similar to, but not identical, to a Panther Ausf.G. The engine deck plate does not have countersunk bolts, the fuel and water filler caps are the same size, and the air intake cowl is retained by only four bolts. (HLD)

Some of the Jagdpanther in the finishing hall at M.N.H. photographed in April 1945. In August 1945 these and two others from the M.N.H the finishing hall were completed under the direction British Forces (R.E.M.E). Fgst. Nr.303101 is displayed at The Tank Museum in Bovington. After recovery from a firing range in Germany, the remains of Fgst.Nr.303112 (in the foreground) are at the Museum in Sinsheim. Fgst.Nr.303110 in the background was recovered by the Weald Foundation, where it will eventually also be restored. These Jagdpanther had Flammenvernichter mufflers without cowls and welded guards for the exhaust pipe holes. (NARA)

The last Jagdpanther Ausf.G2 in this assembly line at M.N.H. was Fgst.Nr.303122 (the 42nd in contract 128 planned to be completed in March 1945). It has a Gleitschuh (skid) instead of a return roller behind the final drive housing and the large diameter idler wheel. (TTM)

4. CAD Drawings

Jagdpanther, Panzerjäger Panther (8.8cm Pak 43/3) (Sd.Kfz.173) Ausführung G1

As completed by M.I.A.G. in January 1944

Initial features that were changed during the series production run:

- Twin driver's periscopes with rain guard
- 16mm thick roof plate with 110mm tall armour guards for periscopes
- 20mm thick base on loader's traversable periscope
- Crew hatches with a single external lock
- Rotating plate for commander's traversable periscopes mounted higher than the cast armour base
- An antenna base and a cap over an air intake hole in the engine deck
- Modified Panther Ausf.A stowage bins mounted on a curved base plate and hung by straps over the tail plate
- 15 ton jack stored horizontally
- Chains with clips to secure the rear end of tow cables

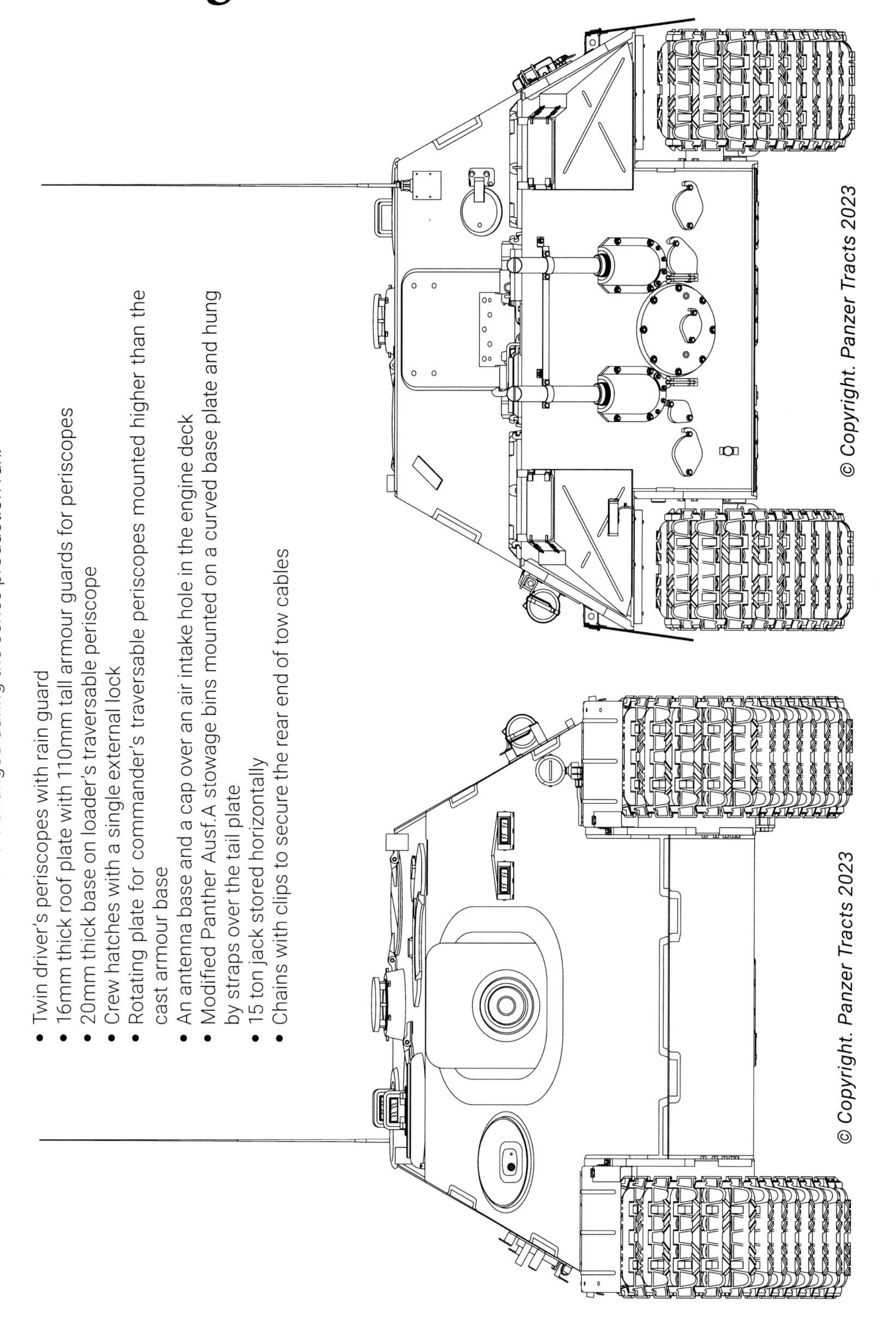

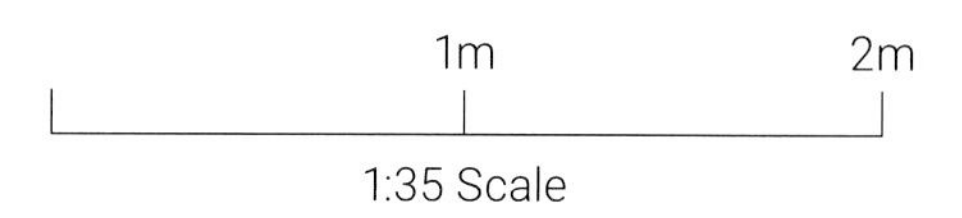

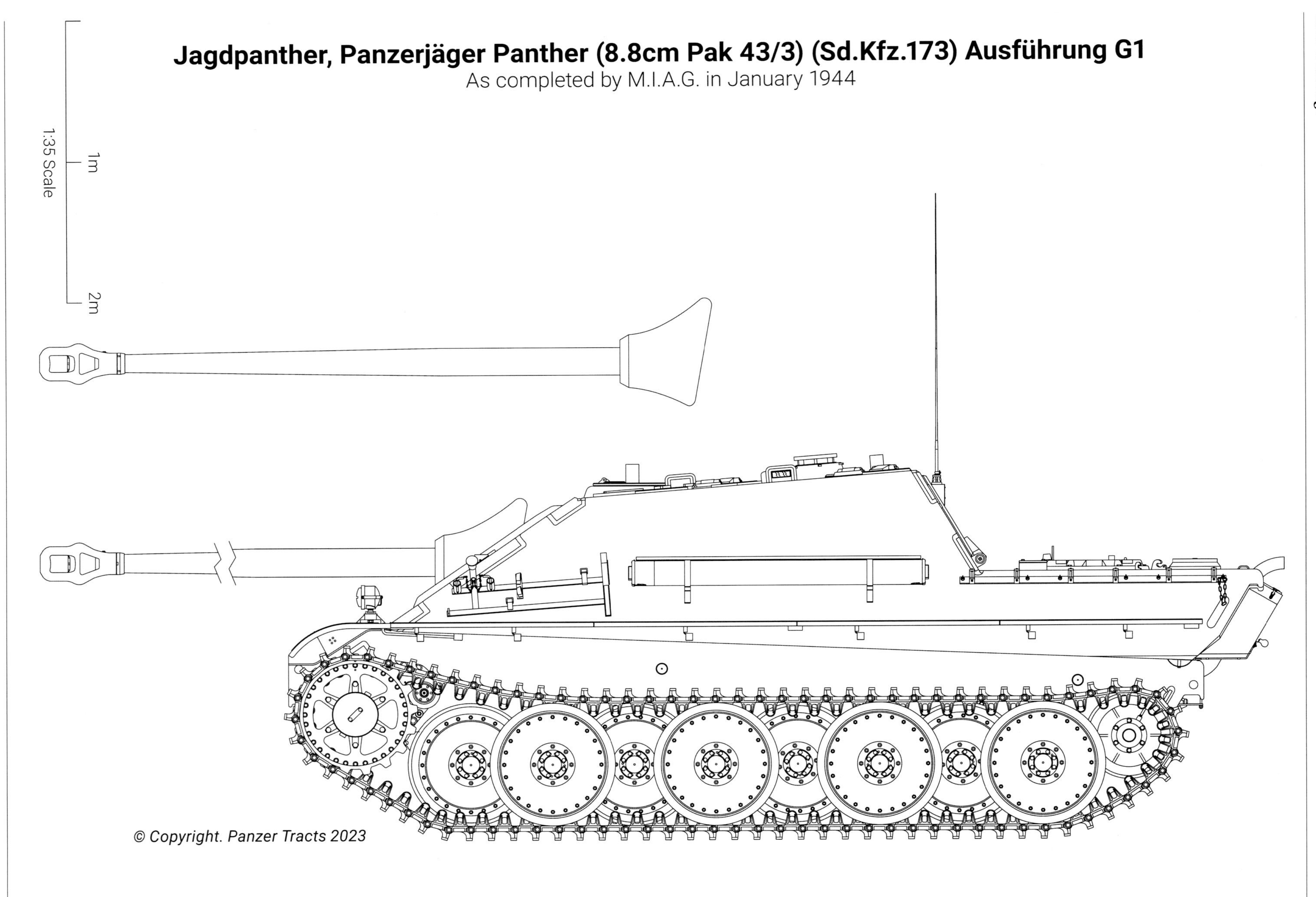

Jagdpanther, Panzerjäger Panther (8.8cm Pak 43/3) (Sd.Kfz.173) Ausführung G1
As completed by M.I.A.G. in January 1944
1m
2m
1:35 Scale
© Copyright. Panzer Tracts 2023

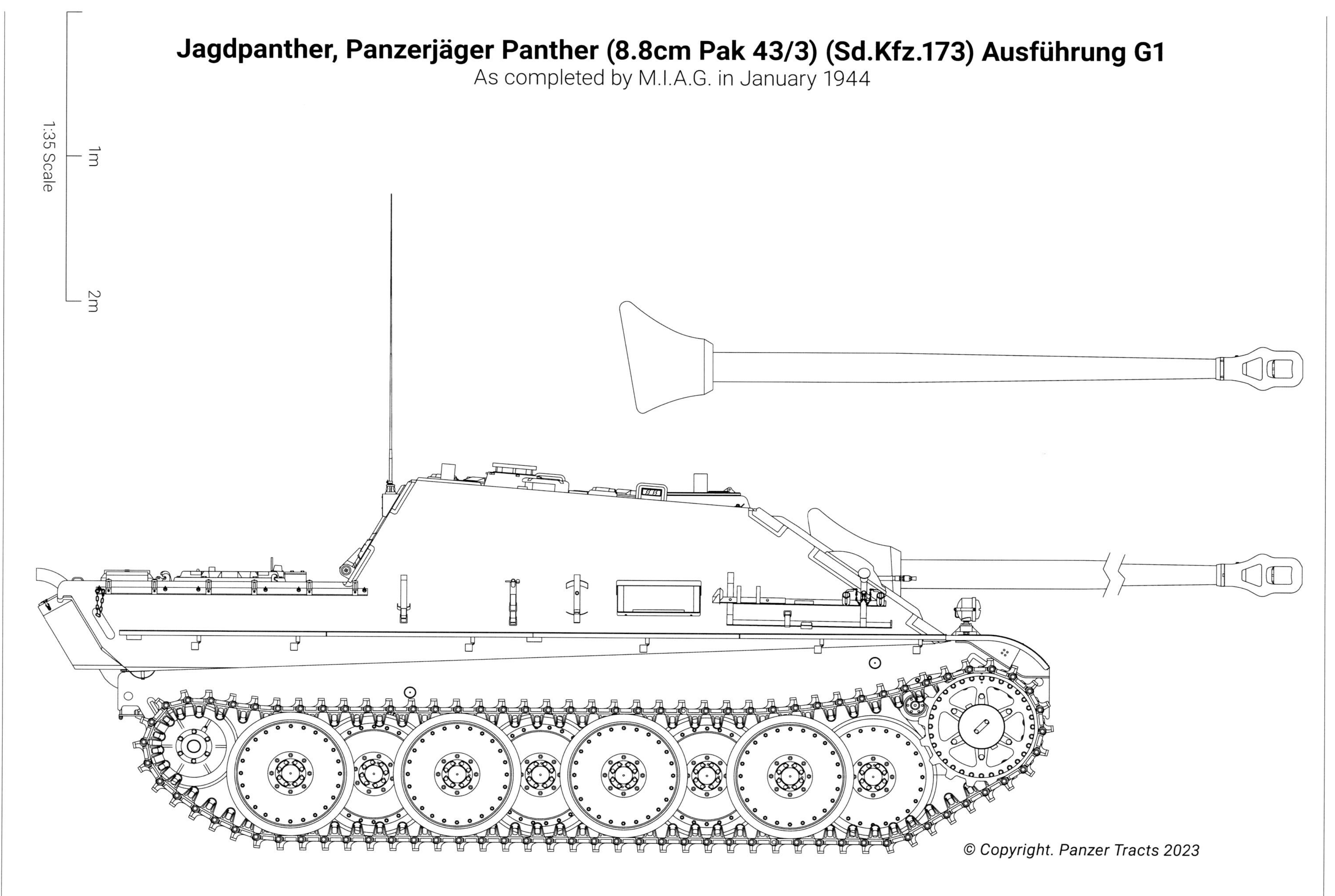
Jagdpanther, Panzerjäger Panther (8.8cm Pak 43/3) (Sd.Kfz.173) Ausführung G1
As completed by M.I.A.G. in January 1944
1:35 Scale
1m
2m
© Copyright. Panzer Tracts 2023

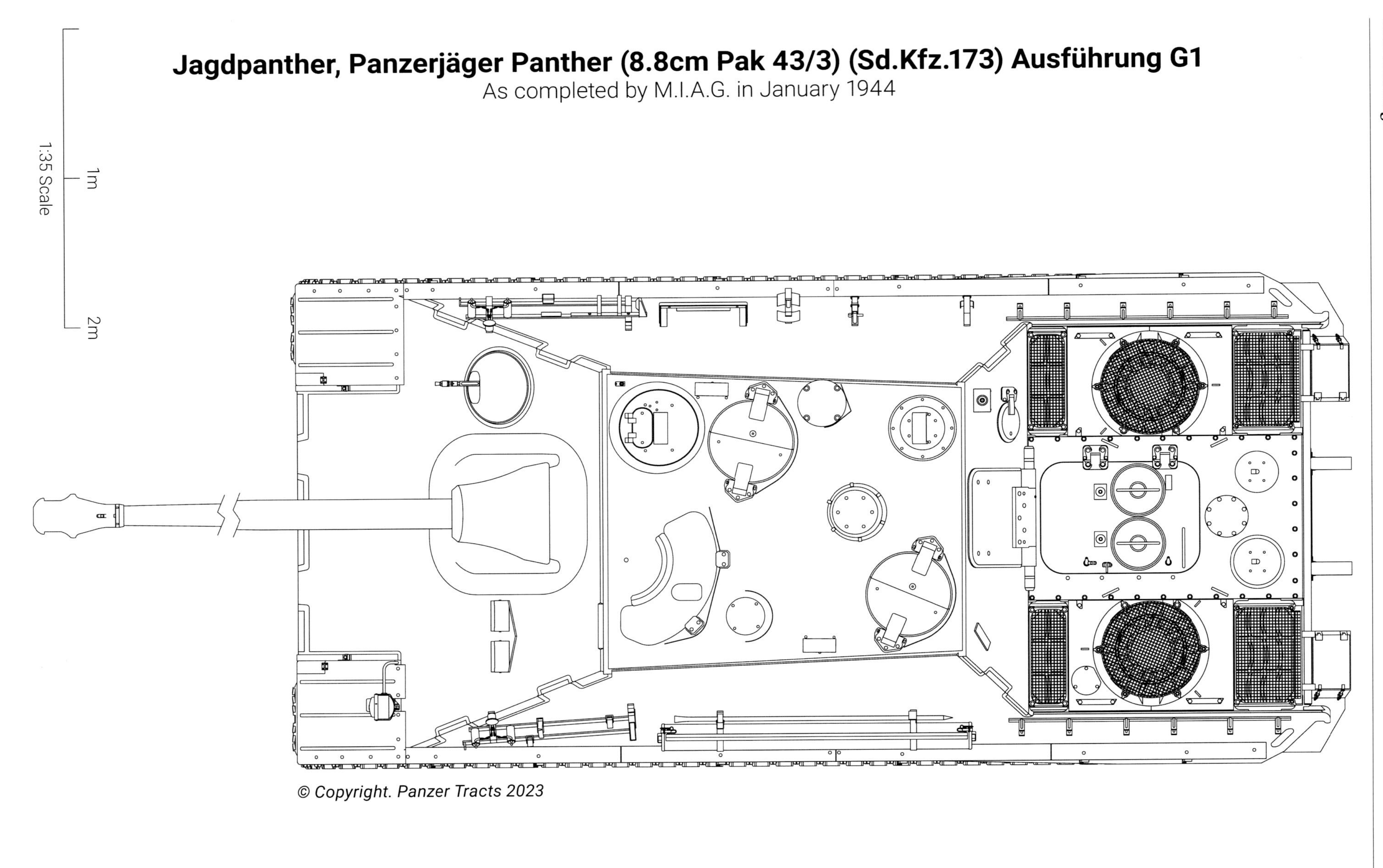
Jagdpanther, Panzerjäger Panther (8.8cm Pak 43/3) (Sd.Kfz.173) Ausführung G1
As completed by M.I.A.G. in January 1944
1m
2m
1:35 Scale
© Copyright. Panzer Tracts 2023

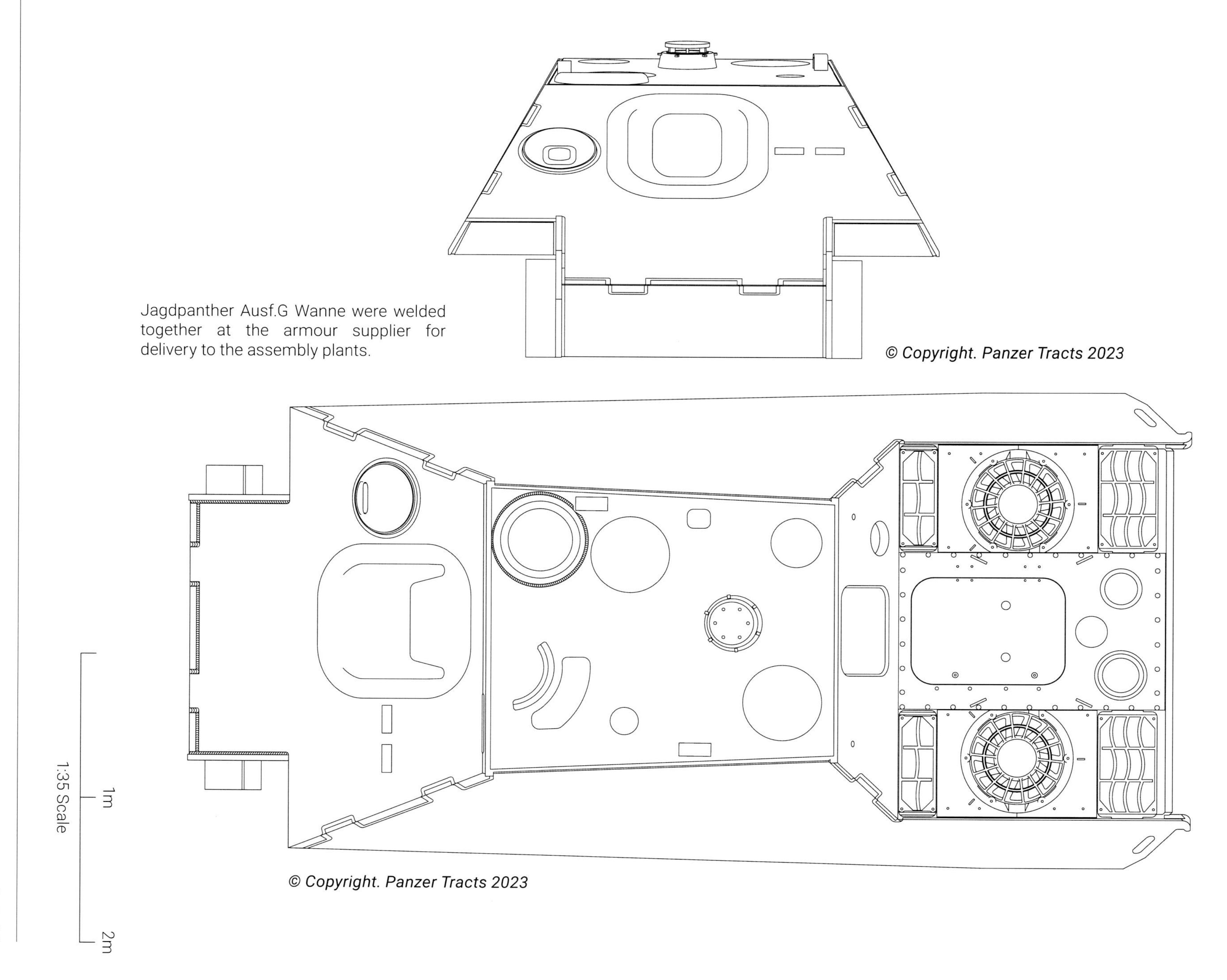

Jagdpanther Ausf.G Wanne were welded together at the armour supplier for delivery to the assembly plants.

This belly from near the start of the Jagdpanther Ausf.G1 production run was constructed by welding a 25mm thick plate at the front, followed by a single 16mm thick plate at the rear. Each pannier was made out of a single 16mm thick plate.

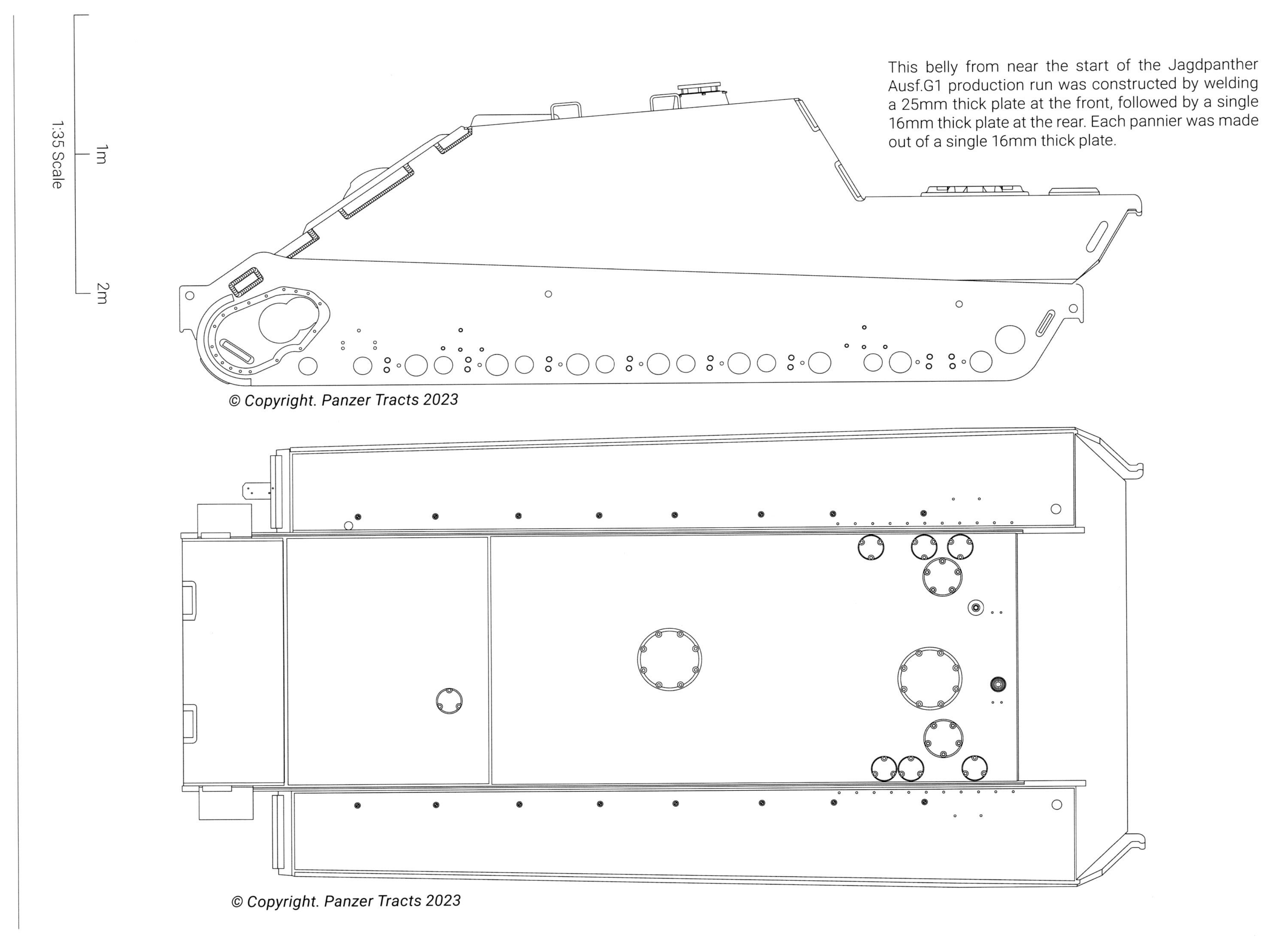

Jagdpanther, Panzerjäger Panther (8.8cm Pak 43/3) (Sd.Kfz.173) (als Panzerjäger-Befehlswagen)
Ausführung G1

As completed by M.I.A.G. in July 1944

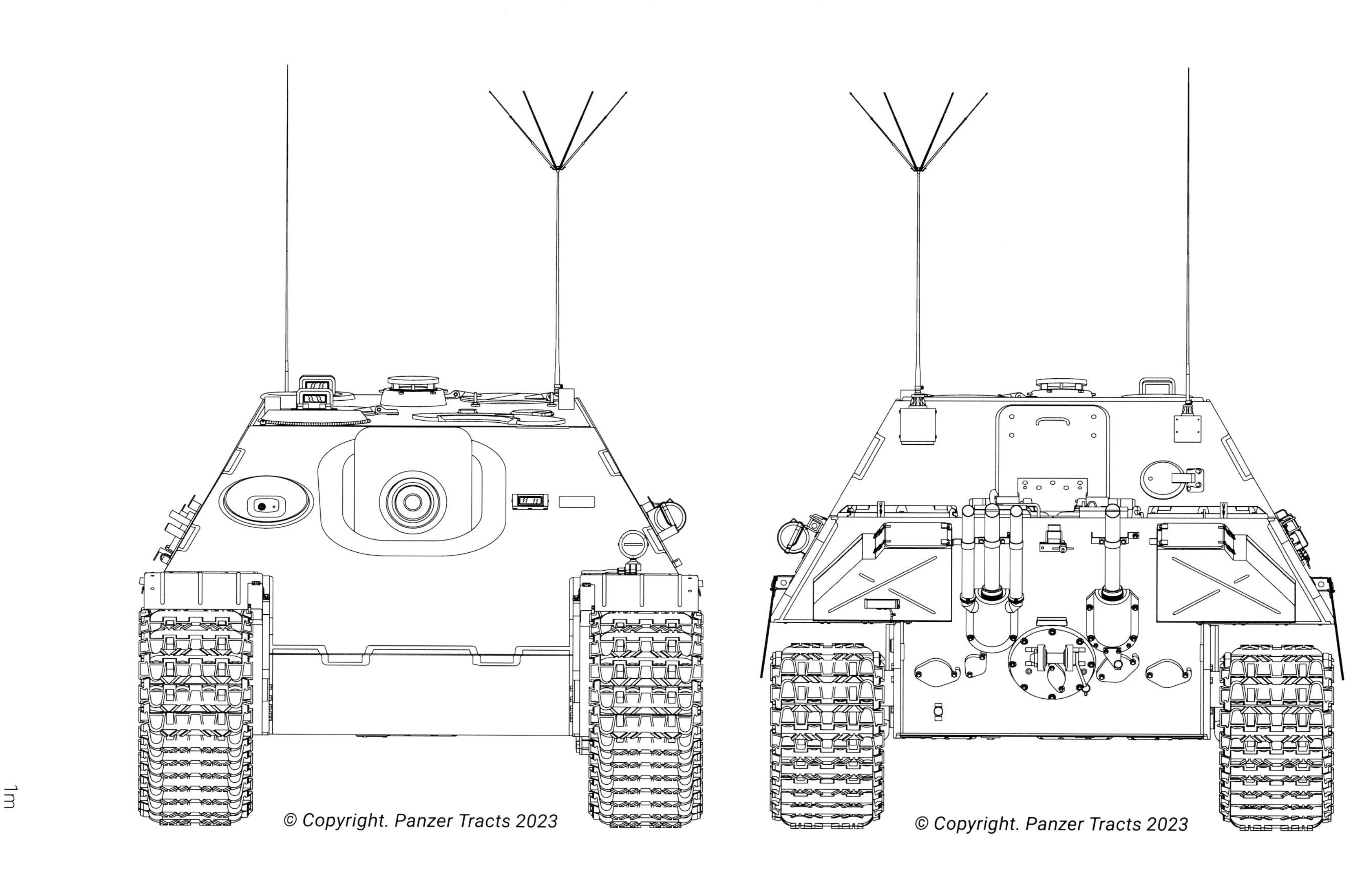

Jagdpanther, Panzerjäger Panther (8.8cm Pak 43/3) (Sd.Kfz.173) (als Panzerjäger-Befehlswagen)
Ausführung G1

As completed by M.I.A.G. in July 1944

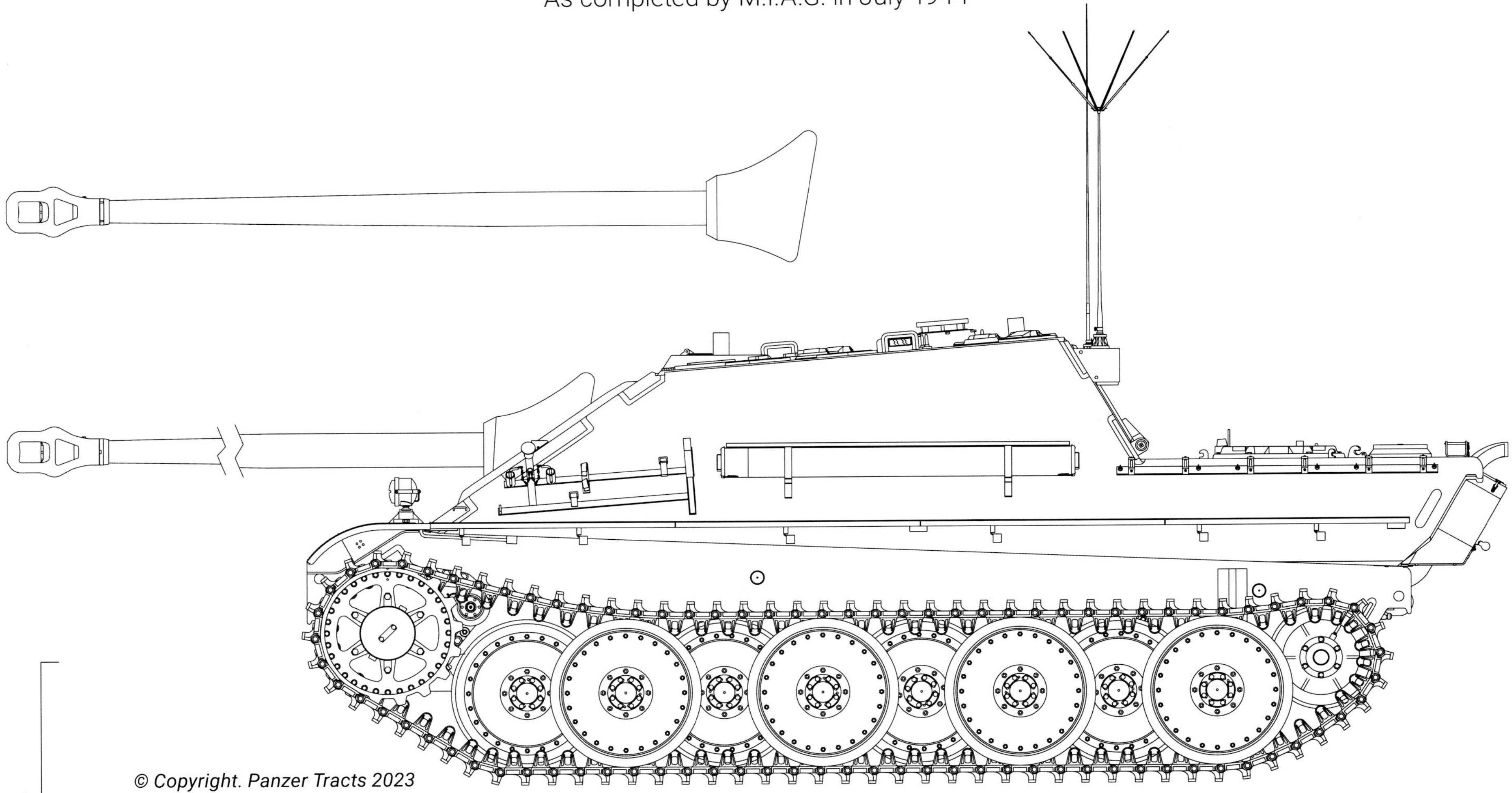

Features present on this 'Befehls-Jagdpanther' include:

- Single driver's periscope with second hole capped
- 25mm thick roof plate with 110mm tall armour guards for periscopes
- 25mm thick base on loader's traversable periscope
- Crew hatches on roof with double external locks
- Rotating plate for commander's traversable periscopes countersunk into armour base
- Pegs for mounting EM 0.9m R rangefinder
- Sternantenne D on porcelain insulator protected by armour pot
- Panther Ausf.A stowage bins mounted on flat plate and hung in slots welded to the tail plate
- Twin engine cooling pipes mounted parallel to left exhaust pipe
- 20-ton jack stored vertically
- Tow bracket welded to engine access hatch

1m 2m

1:35 Scale

Jagdpanther, Panzerjäger Panther (8.8cm Pak 43/3) (Sd.Kfz.173) (als Panzerjäger-Befehlswagen)
Ausführung G1
As completed by M.I.A.G. in July 1944

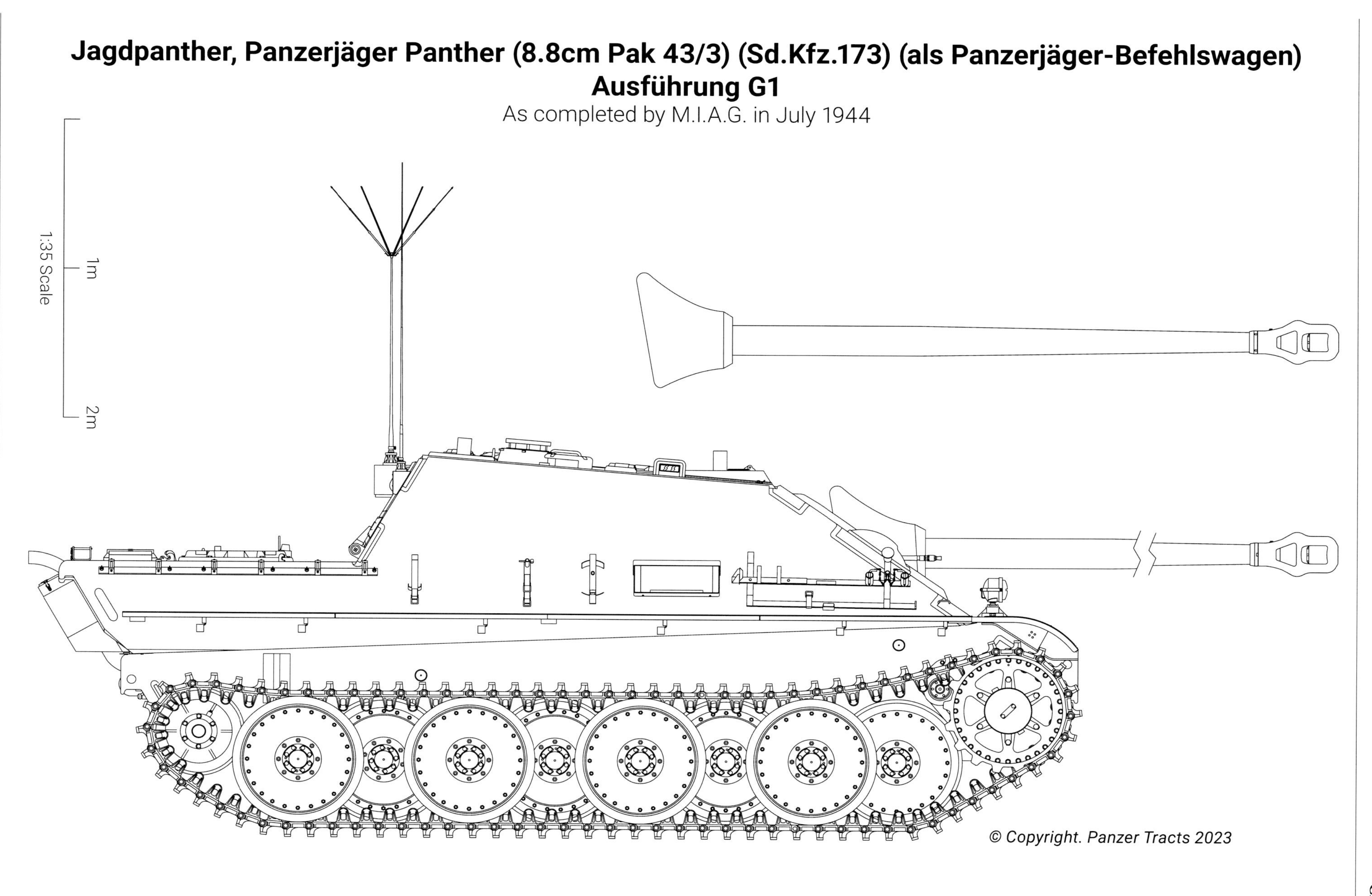

Jagdpanther, Panzerjäger Panther (8.8cm Pak 43/3) (Sd.Kfz.173) (als Panzerjäger-Befehlswagen)
Ausführung G1

As completed by M.I.A.G. in July 1944

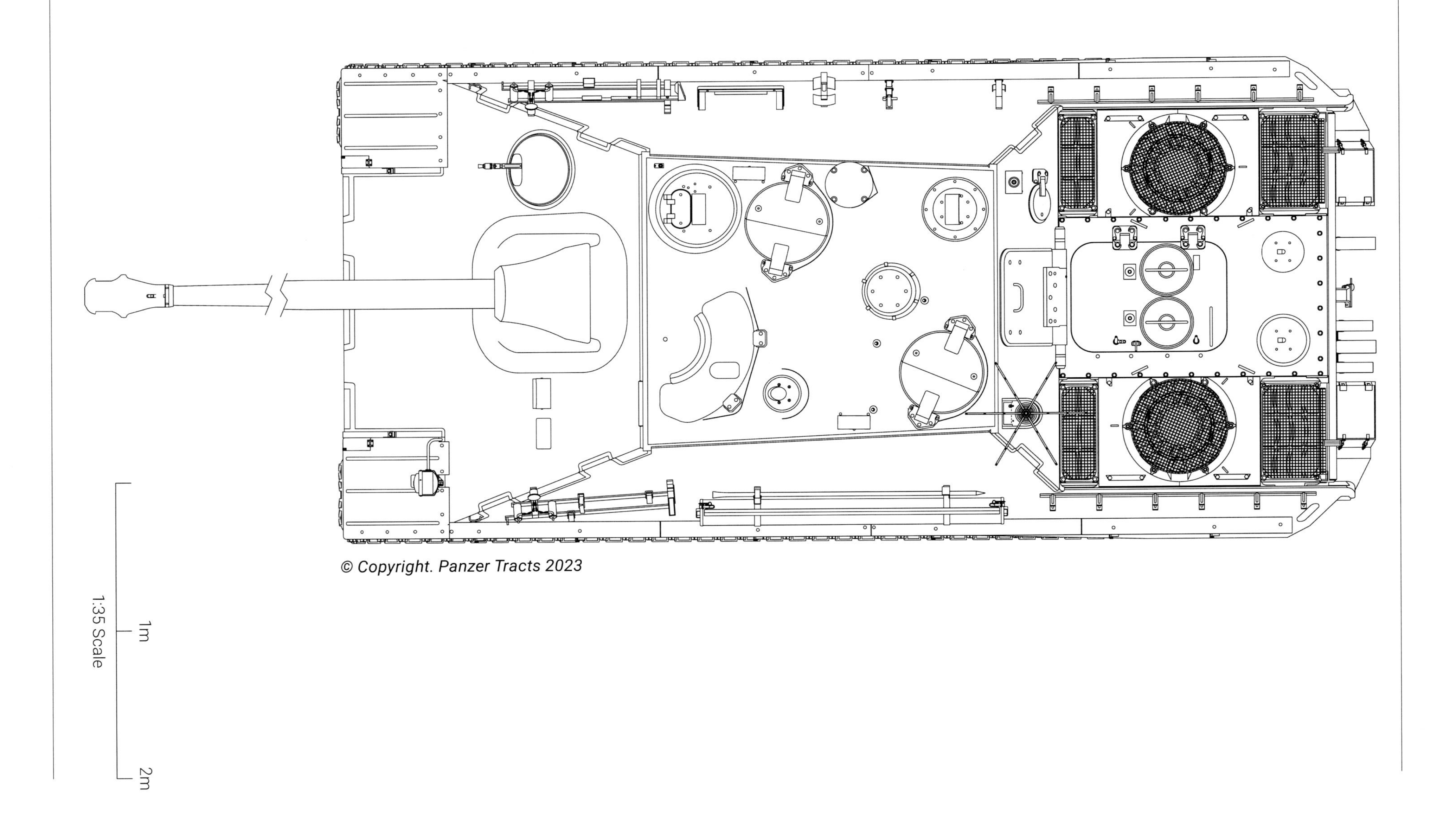

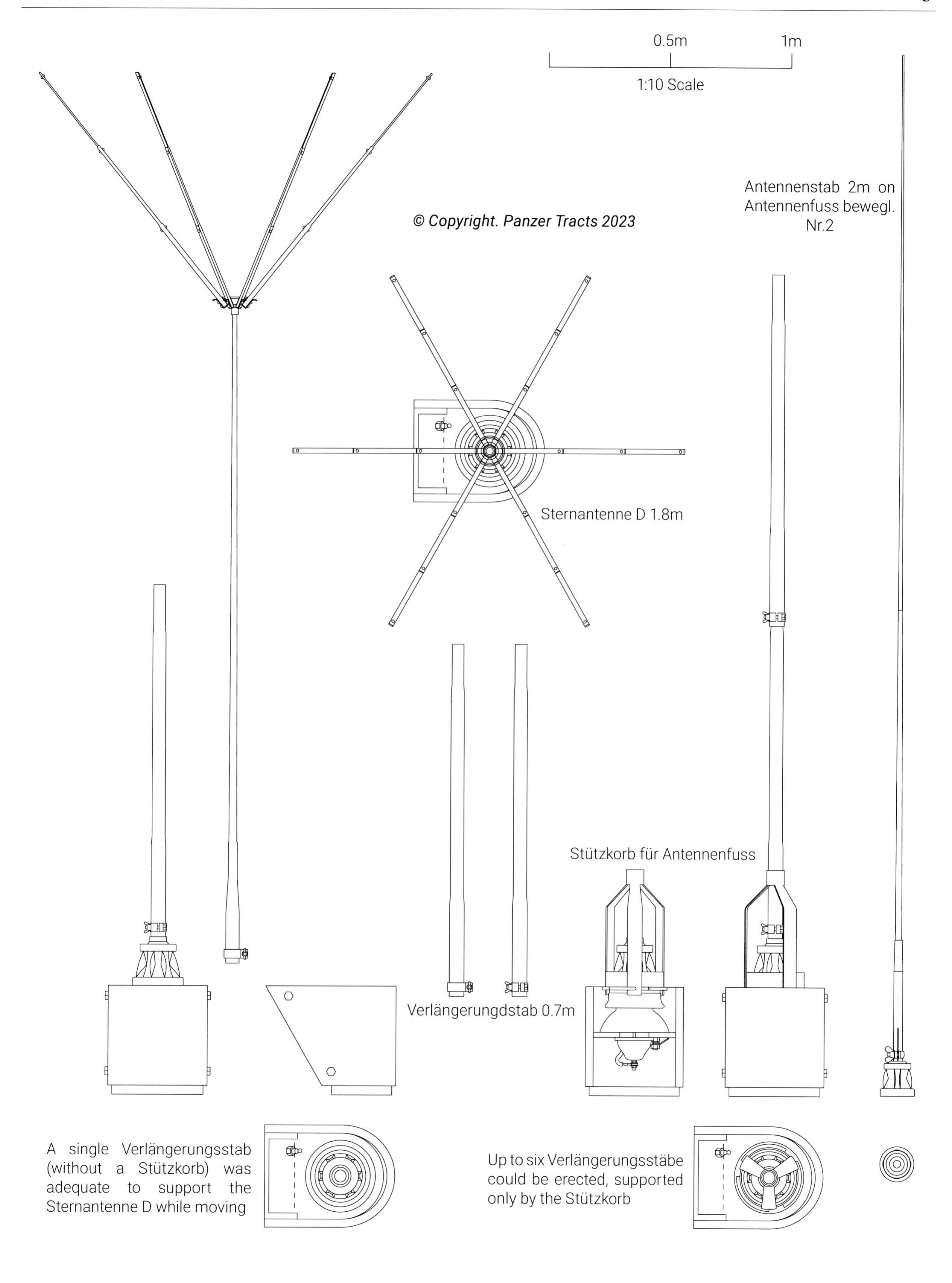

A single Verlängerungsstab (without a Stützkorb) was adequate to support the Sternantenne D while moving

Up to six Verlängerungsstäbe could be erected, supported only by the Stützkorb

Jagdpanther, Panzerjäger Panther (8.8cm Pak 43/3) (Sd.Kfz.173) Ausführung G1

As completed by M.N.H. in November/December 1944

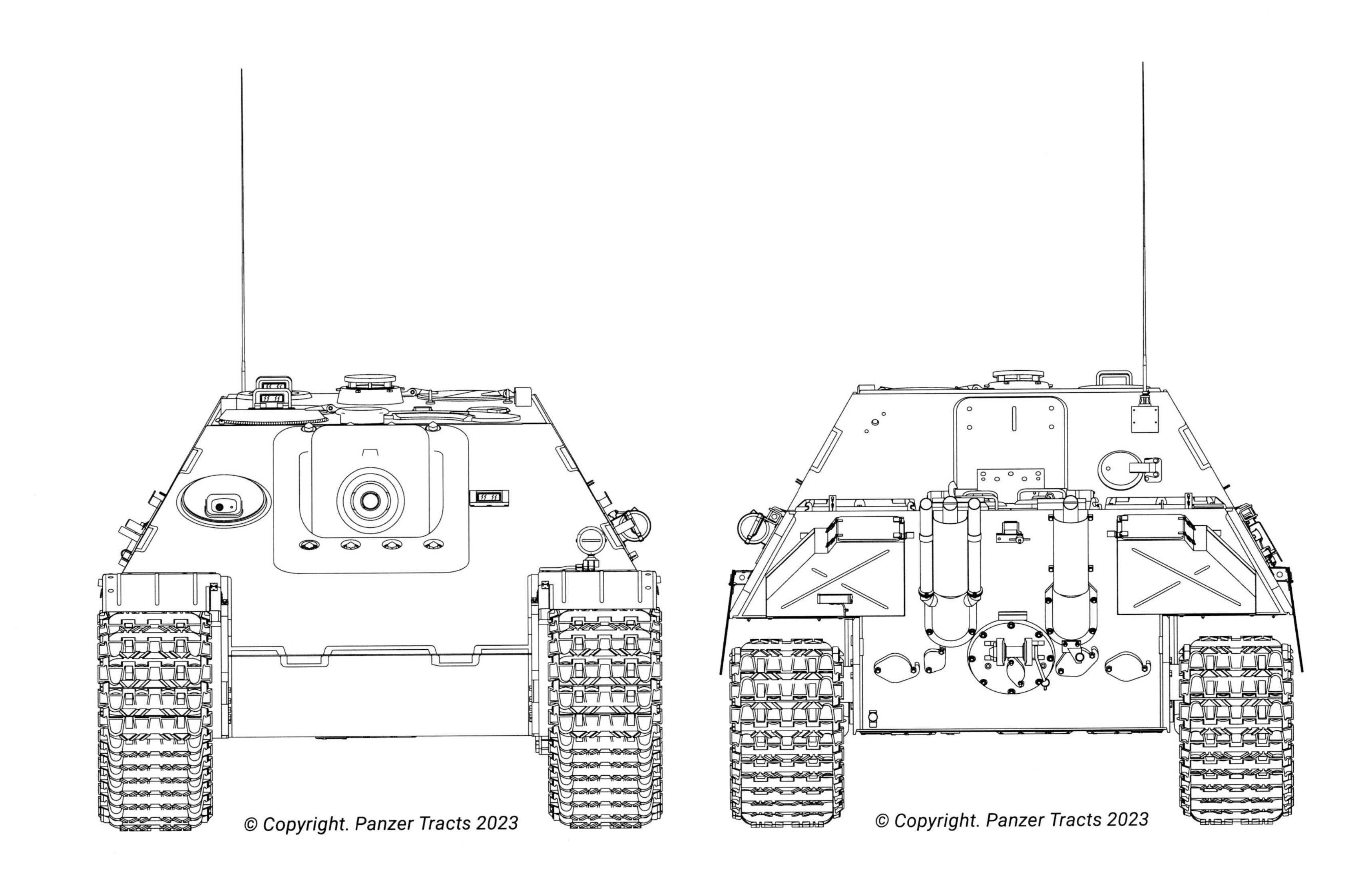

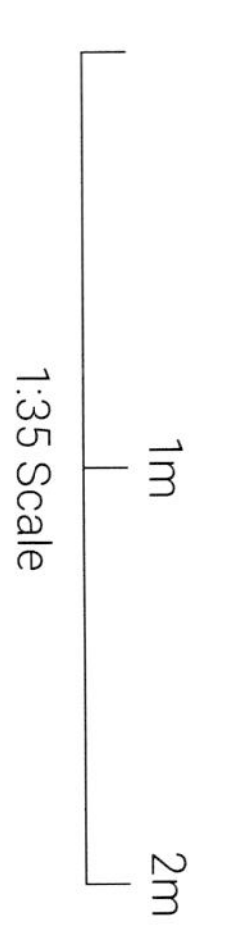

Jagdpanther, Panzerjäger Panther (8.8cm Pak 43/3) (Sd.Kfz.173) Ausführung G1

As completed by M.N.H. in November/December 1944

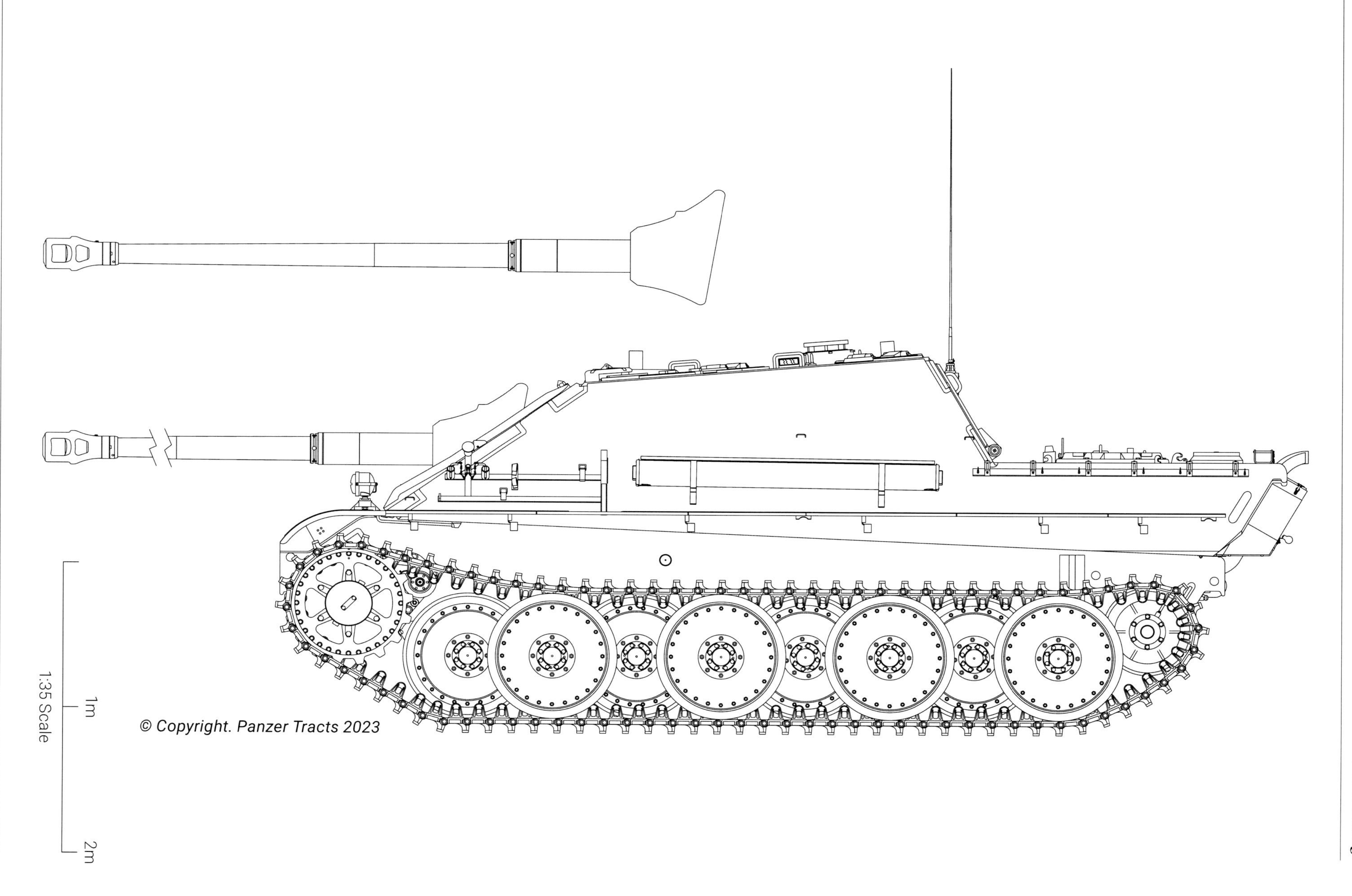

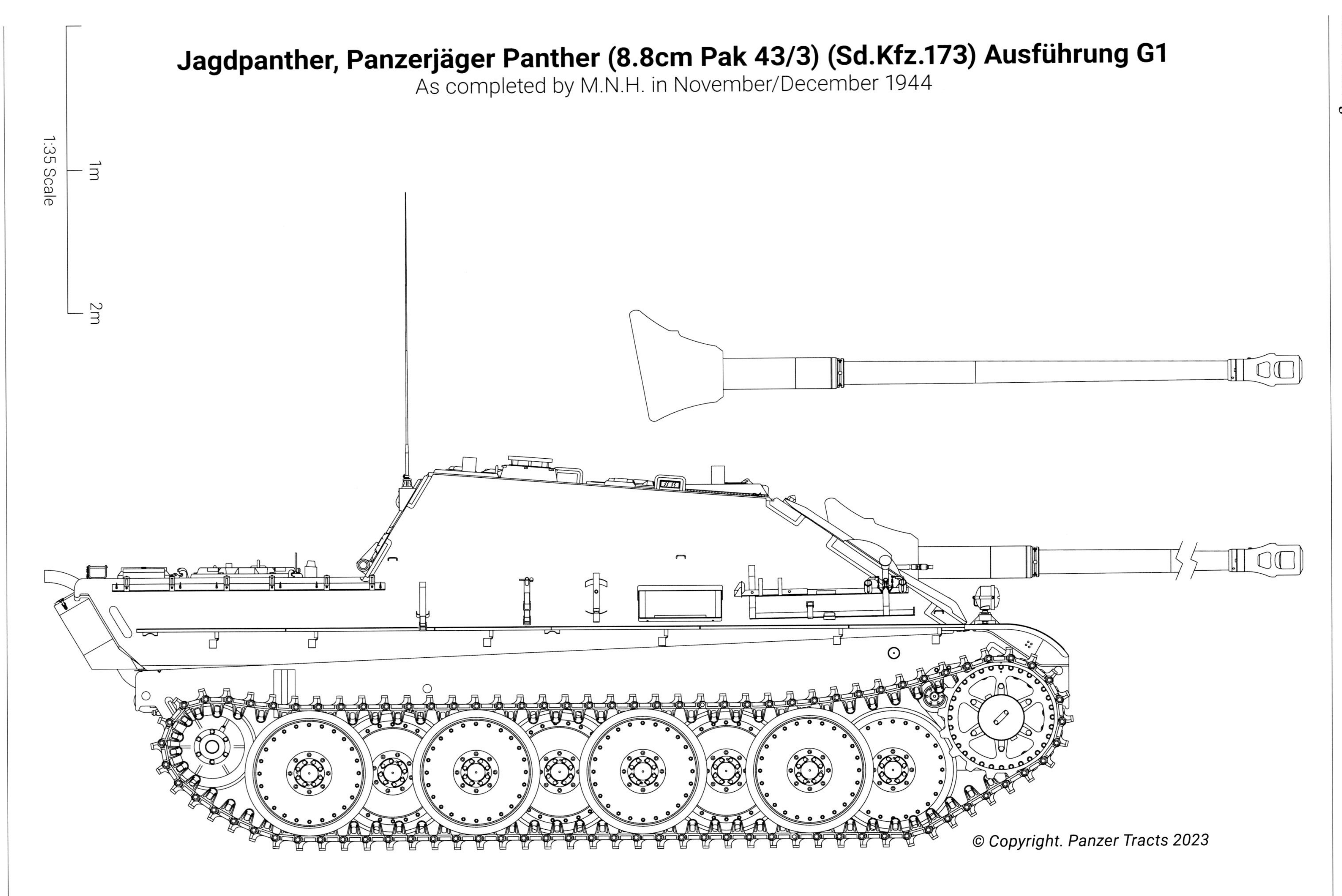
Jagdpanther, Panzerjäger Panther (8.8cm Pak 43/3) (Sd.Kfz.173) Ausführung G1
As completed by M.N.H. in November/December 1944
1m
2m
1:35 Scale
© Copyright. Panzer Tracts 2023

Jagdpanther, Panzerjäger Panther (8.8cm Pak 43/3) (Sd.Kfz.173) Ausführung G1

As completed by M.N.H. in November/December 1944

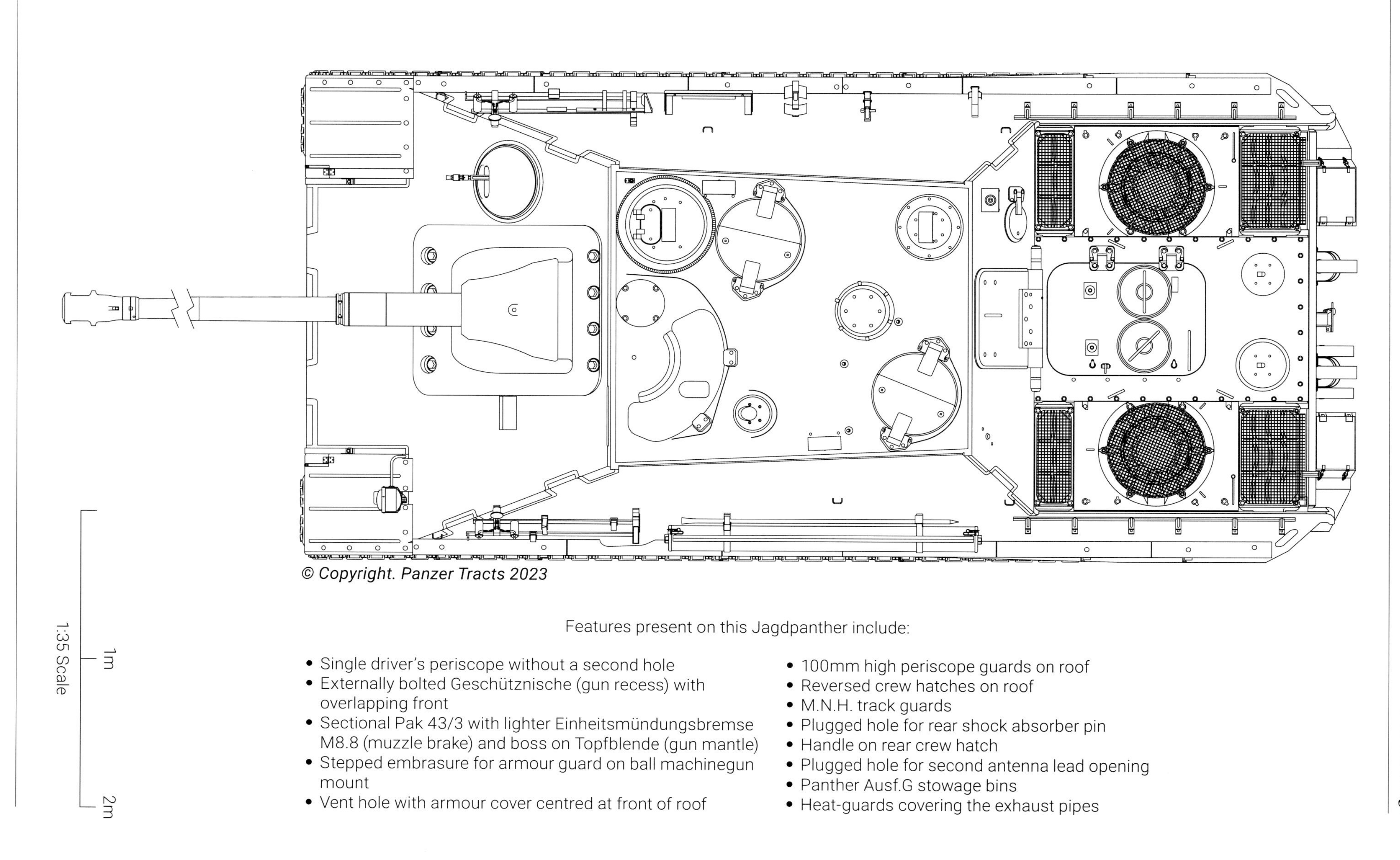

Features present on this Jagdpanther include:

- Single driver's periscope without a second hole
- Externally bolted Geschütznische (gun recess) with overlapping front
- Sectional Pak 43/3 with lighter Einheitsmündungsbremse M8.8 (muzzle brake) and boss on Topfblende (gun mantle)
- Stepped embrasure for armour guard on ball machinegun mount
- Vent hole with armour cover centred at front of roof
- 100mm high periscope guards on roof
- Reversed crew hatches on roof
- M.N.H. track guards
- Plugged hole for rear shock absorber pin
- Handle on rear crew hatch
- Plugged hole for second antenna lead opening
- Panther Ausf.G stowage bins
- Heat-guards covering the exhaust pipes

Jagdpanther, Panzerjäger Panther (8.8cm Pak 43/3) (Sd.Kfz.173) Ausführung G2

As completed by M.N.H. in March/April 1945

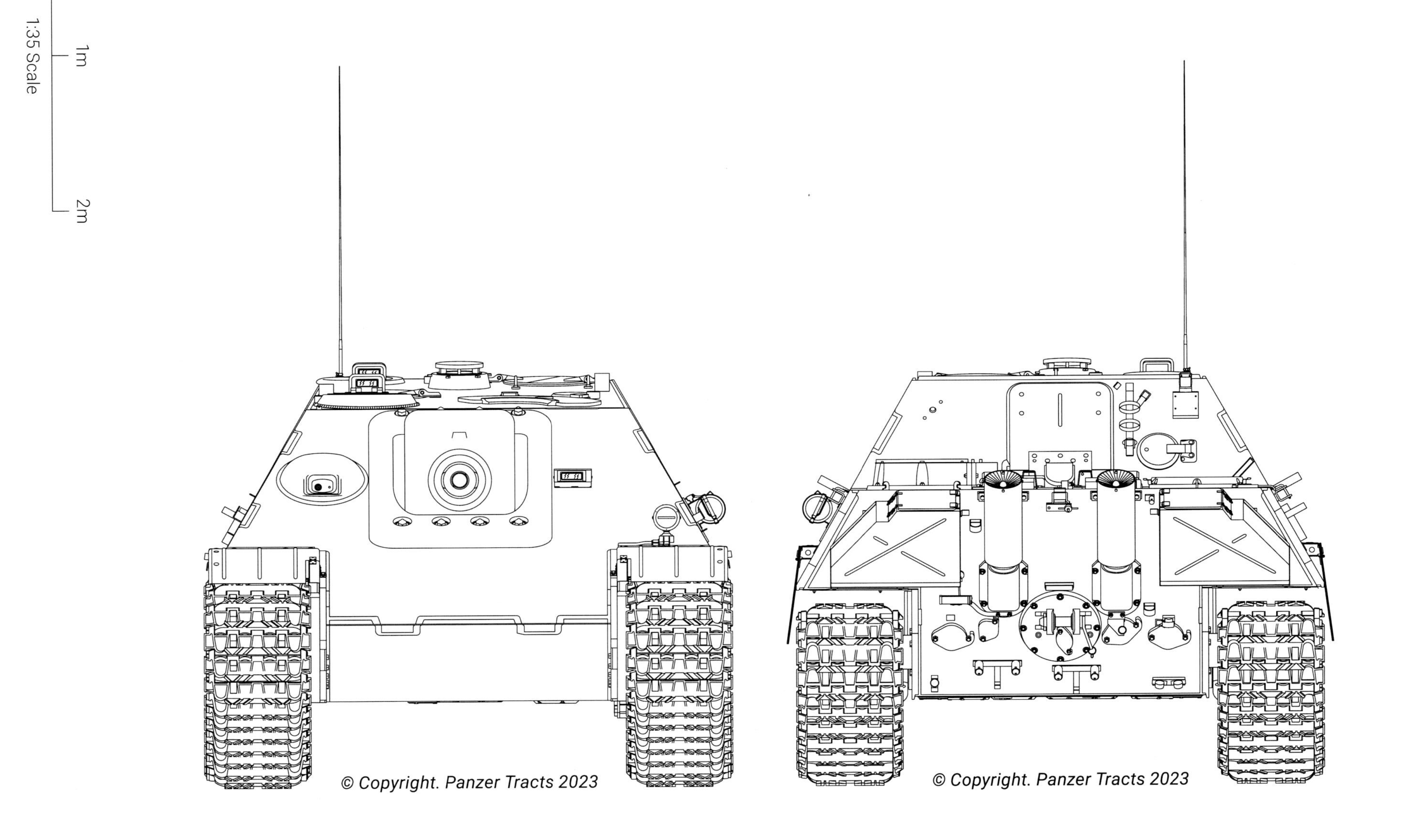

Jagdpanther, Panzerjäger Panther (8.8cm Pak 43/3) (Sd.Kfz.173) Ausführung G2

As completed by M.N.H. in March/April 1945

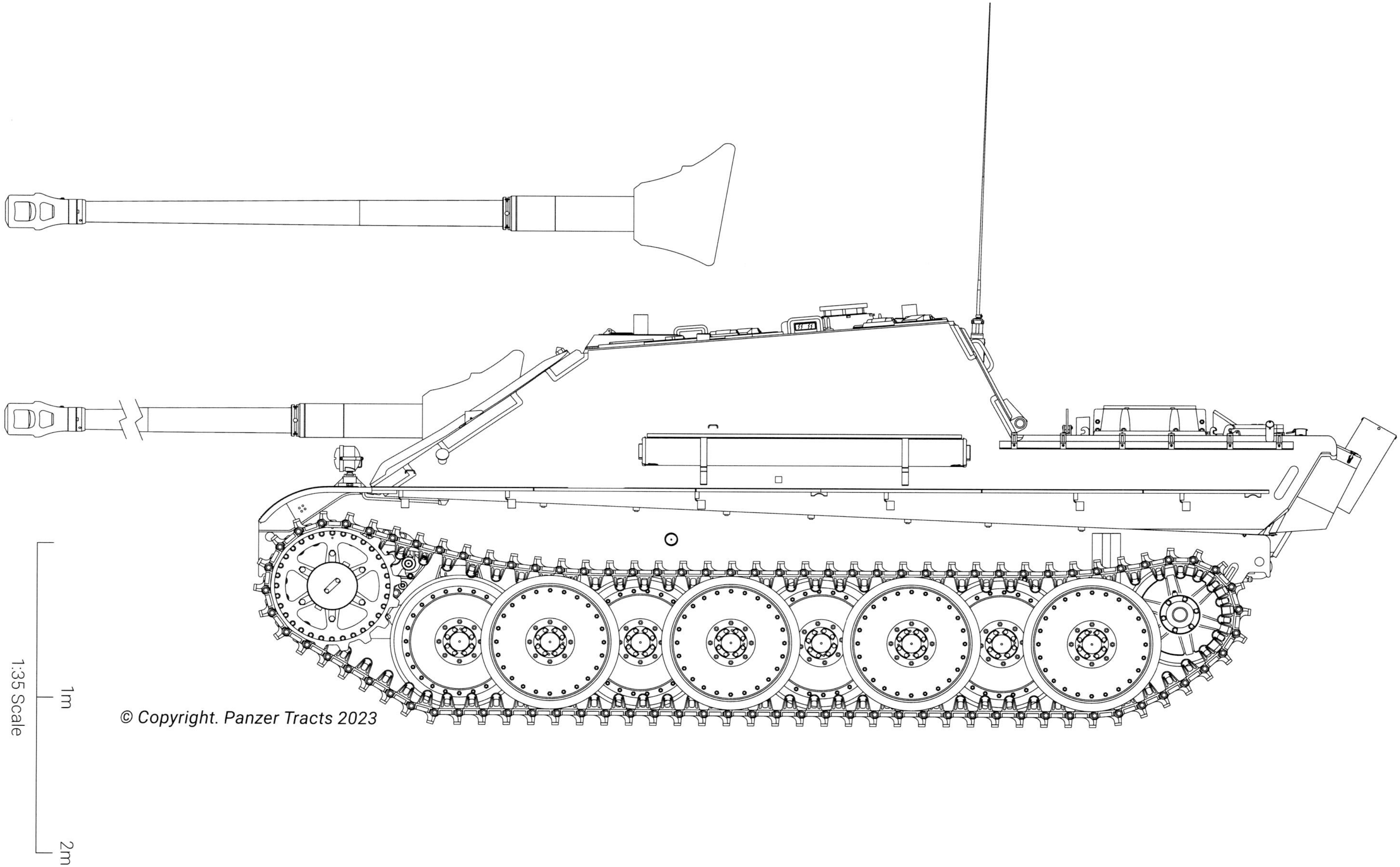

1m 2m

1:35 Scale

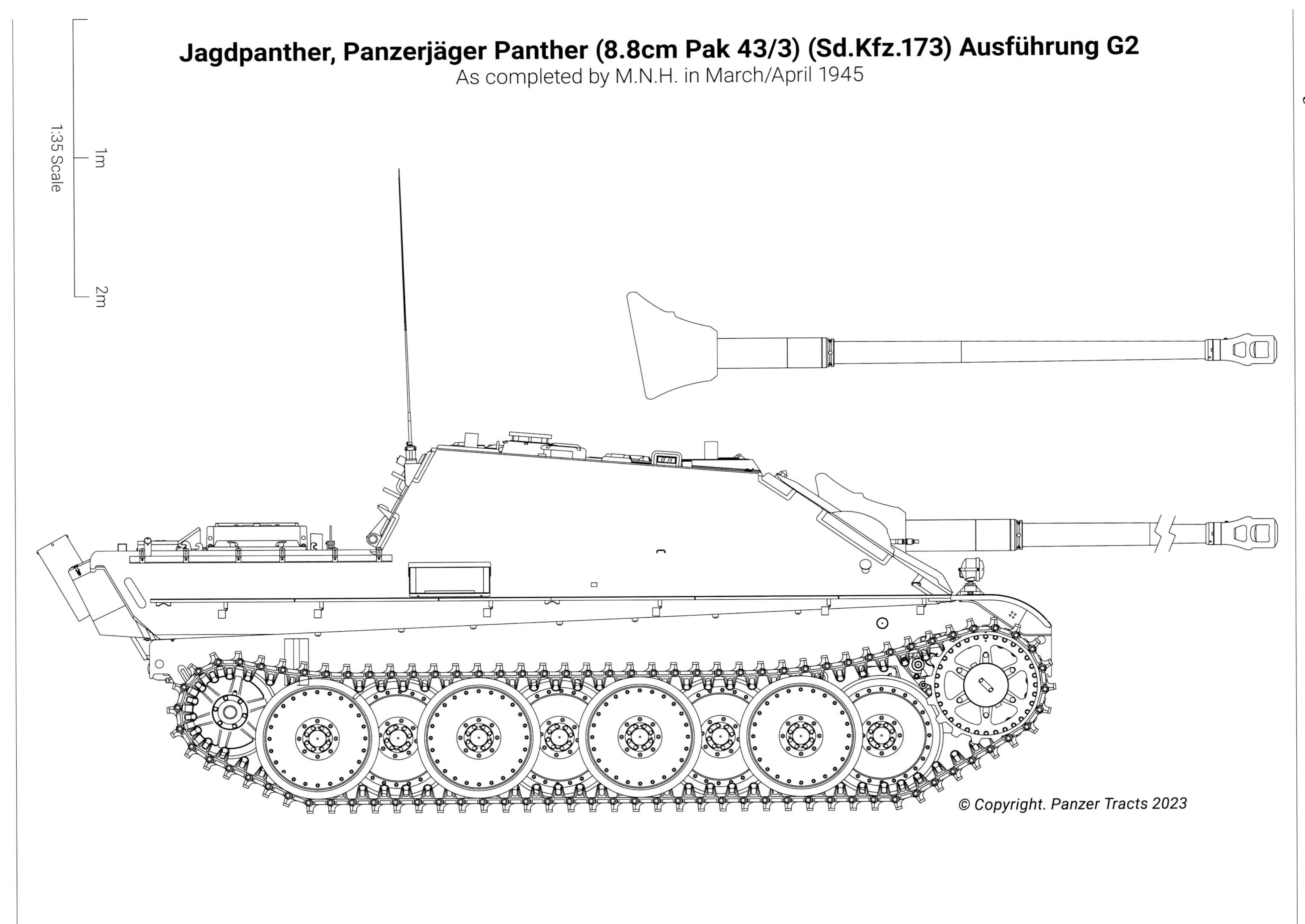
Jagdpanther, Panzerjäger Panther (8.8cm Pak 43/3) (Sd.Kfz.173) Ausführung G2
As completed by M.N.H. in March/April 1945
1m
2m
1:35 Scale
© Copyright. Panzer Tracts 2023

Jagdpanther, Panzerjäger Panther (8.8cm Pak 43/3) (Sd.Kfz.173) Ausführung G2

As completed by M.N.H. in March/April 1945

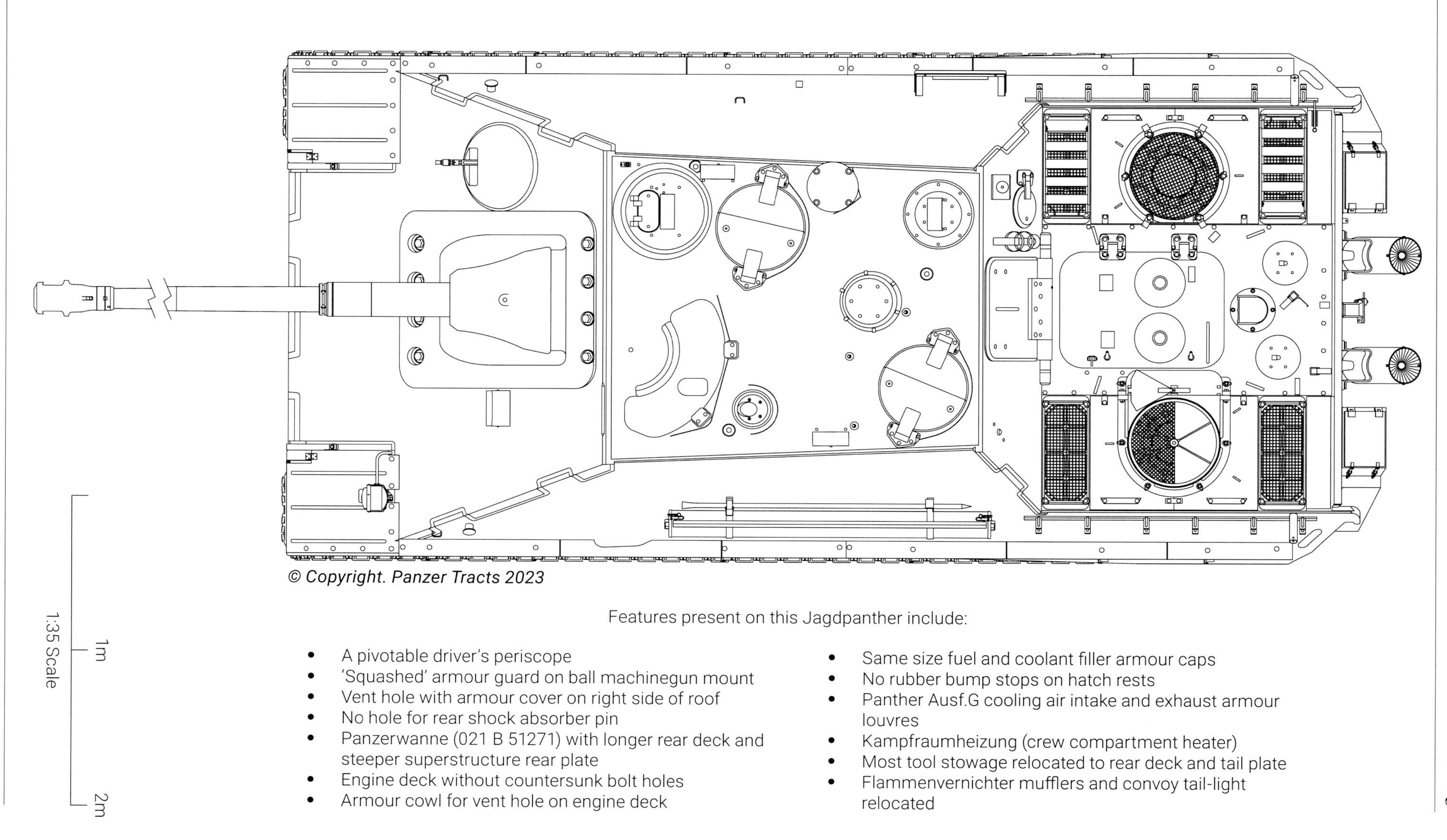

Features present on this Jagdpanther include:

- A pivotable driver's periscope
- 'Squashed' armour guard on ball machinegun mount
- Vent hole with armour cover on right side of roof
- No hole for rear shock absorber pin
- Panzerwanne (021 B 51271) with longer rear deck and steeper superstructure rear plate
- Engine deck without countersunk bolt holes
- Armour cowl for vent hole on engine deck
- Same size fuel and coolant filler armour caps
- No rubber bump stops on hatch rests
- Panther Ausf.G cooling air intake and exhaust armour louvres
- Kampfraumheizung (crew compartment heater)
- Most tool stowage relocated to rear deck and tail plate
- Flammenvernichter mufflers and convoy tail-light relocated

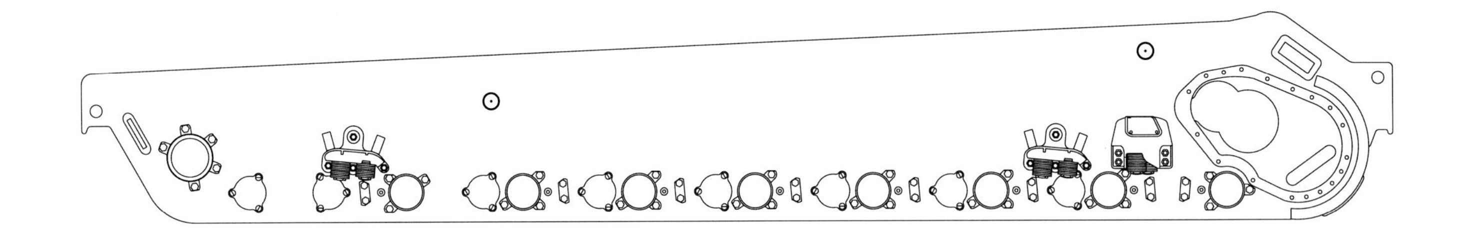

Above and Below: A partially assembled Jagdpanther Fahrgestell from near the start of the production series. Caps with three bolts covered the access holes for offside torsion bars. A total of six bolts were used to retain internal torsion bar fittings and the end of the second torsion bar of each pair. There were three bump stops with Belleville washers for the 1st, 2nd, and 7th left and 8th right swing arms.

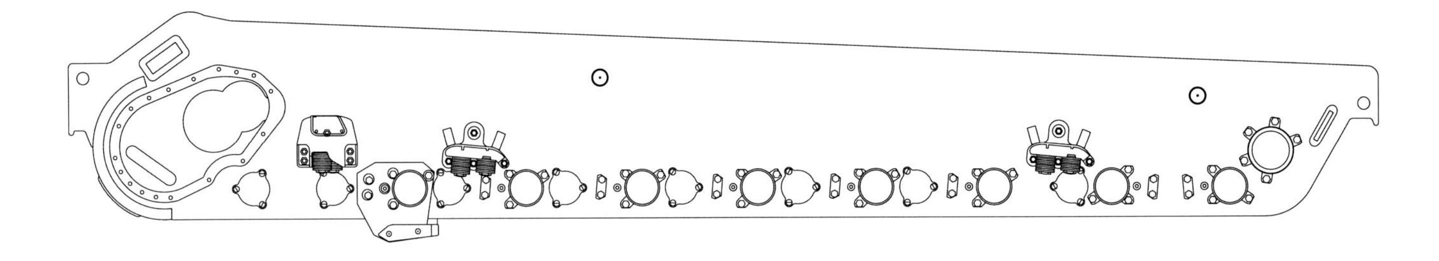

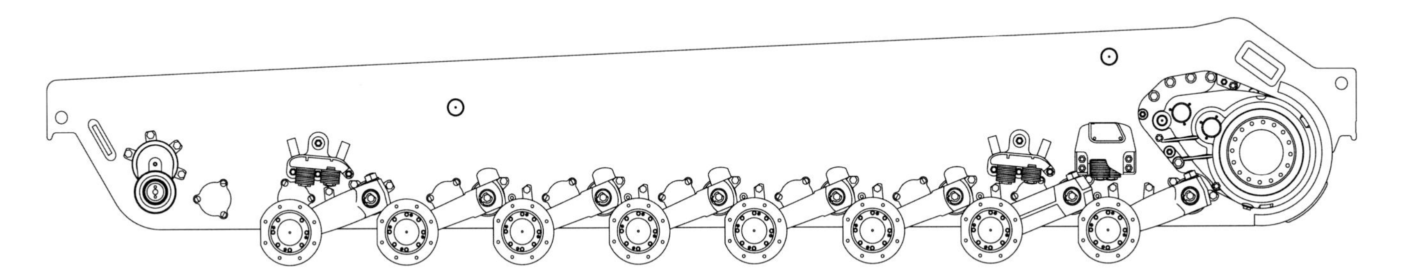

Above and Below: A partially assembled Jagdpanther Fahrgestell from near the start of the production series. Three different swing arms were used - verstärkte Siepmann-Kurbel (021 St 48393-40) on the 1st, 7th left and 8th right stations, verstärkte Bochumer-Vereins-Kurbel (021 St 48393-14) on the 2nd stations, and normale Siepmann-Hohlkurbel (021 St 48303-30) on all other stations.

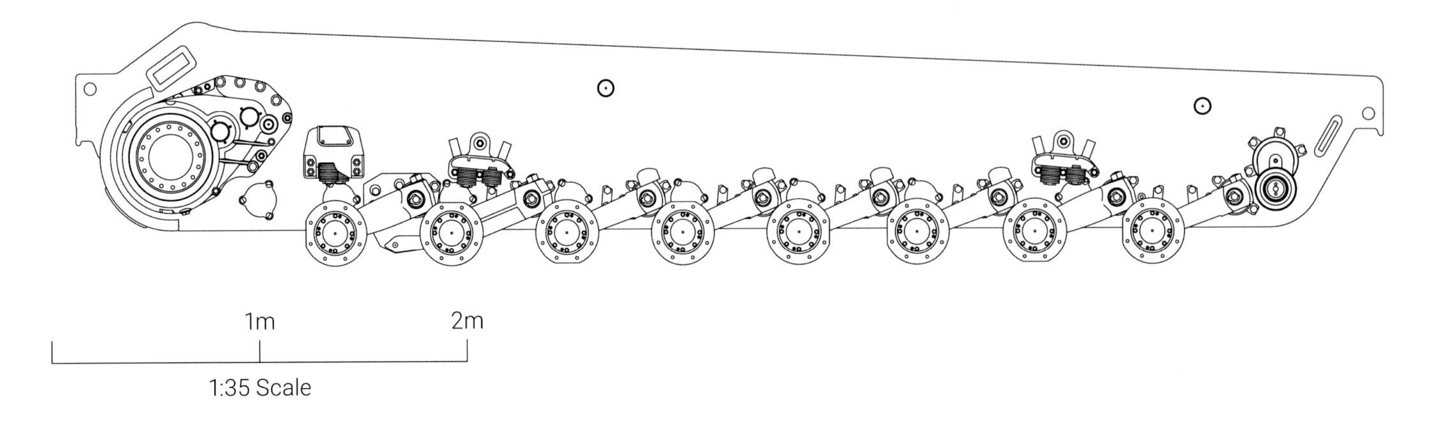

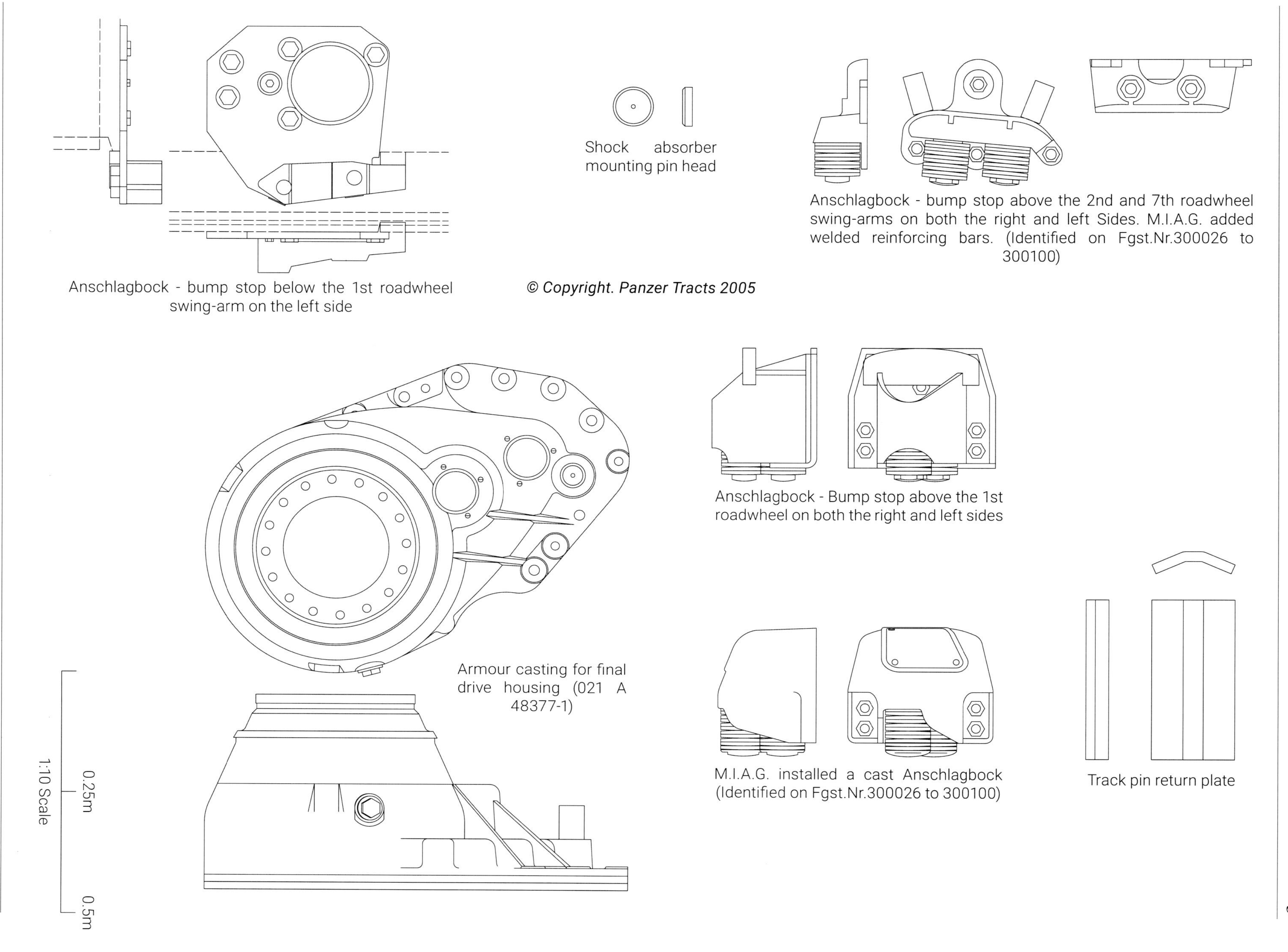
Shock absorber mounting pin head
Anschlagbock - bump stop above the 2nd and 7th roadwheel swing-arms on both the right and left Sides. M.I.A.G. added welded reinforcing bars. (Identified on Fgst.Nr.300026 to 300100)
Anschlagbock - bump stop below the 1st roadwheel swing-arm on the left side
© Copyright. Panzer Tracts 2005
Anschlagbock - Bump stop above the 1st roadwheel on both the right and left sides
Armour casting for final drive housing (021 A 48377-1)
M.I.A.G. installed a cast Anschlagbock (Identified on Fgst.Nr.300026 to 300100)
Track pin return plate
0.25m
0.5m
1:10 Scale

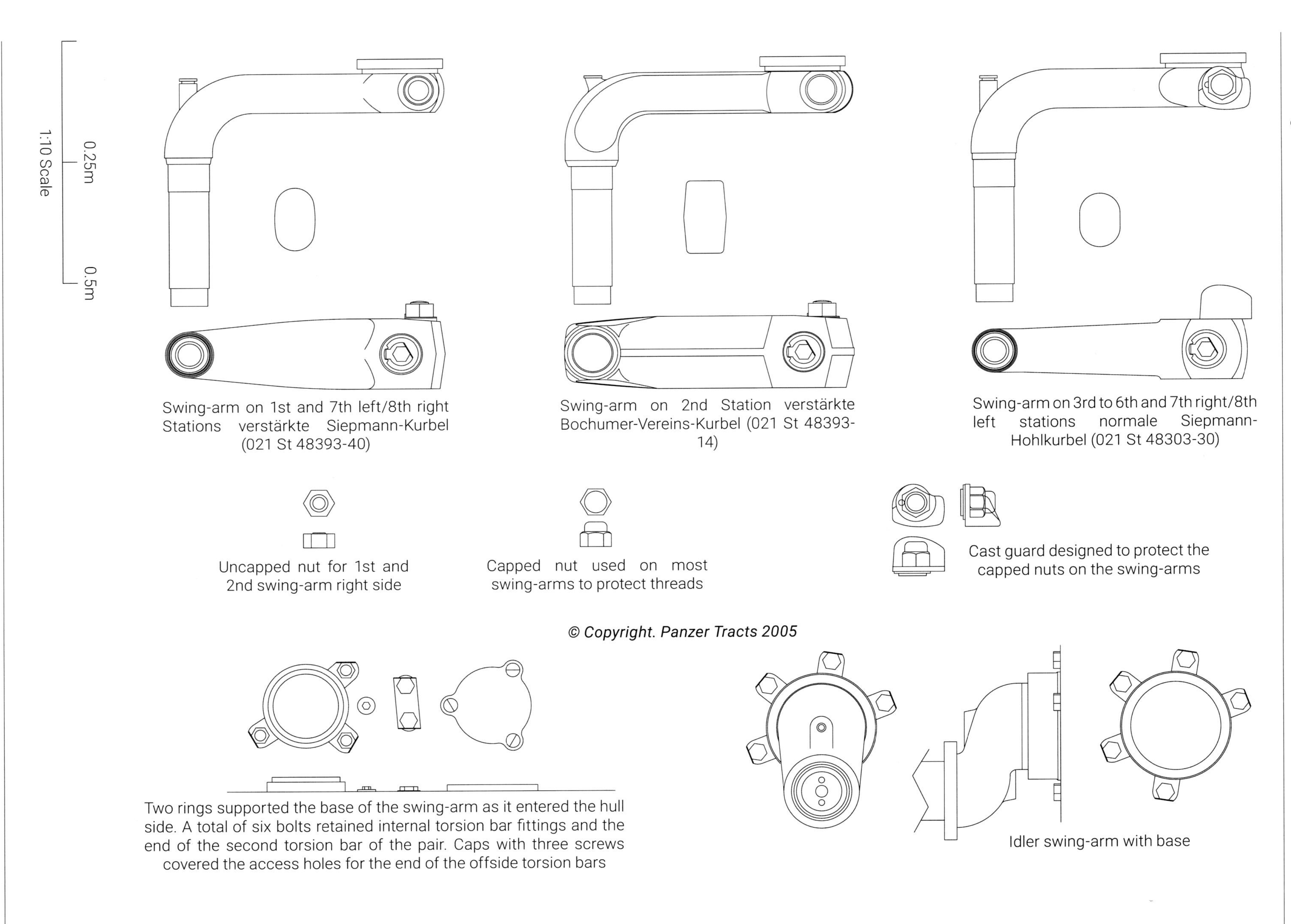

0.25m
0.5m
1:10 Scale
Swing-arm on 1st and 7th left/8th right Stations verstärkte Siepmann-Kurbel (021 St 48393-40)
Swing-arm on 2nd Station verstärkte Bochumer-Vereins-Kurbel (021 St 48393-14)
Swing-arm on 3rd to 6th and 7th right/8th left stations normale Siepmann-Hohlkurbel (021 St 48303-30)
Uncapped nut for 1st and 2nd swing-arm right side
Capped nut used on most swing-arms to protect threads
Cast guard designed to protect the capped nuts on the swing-arms
© Copyright. Panzer Tracts 2005
Two rings supported the base of the swing-arm as it entered the hull side. A total of six bolts retained internal torsion bar fittings and the end of the second torsion bar of the pair. Caps with three screws covered the access holes for the end of the offside torsion bars
Idler swing-arm with base

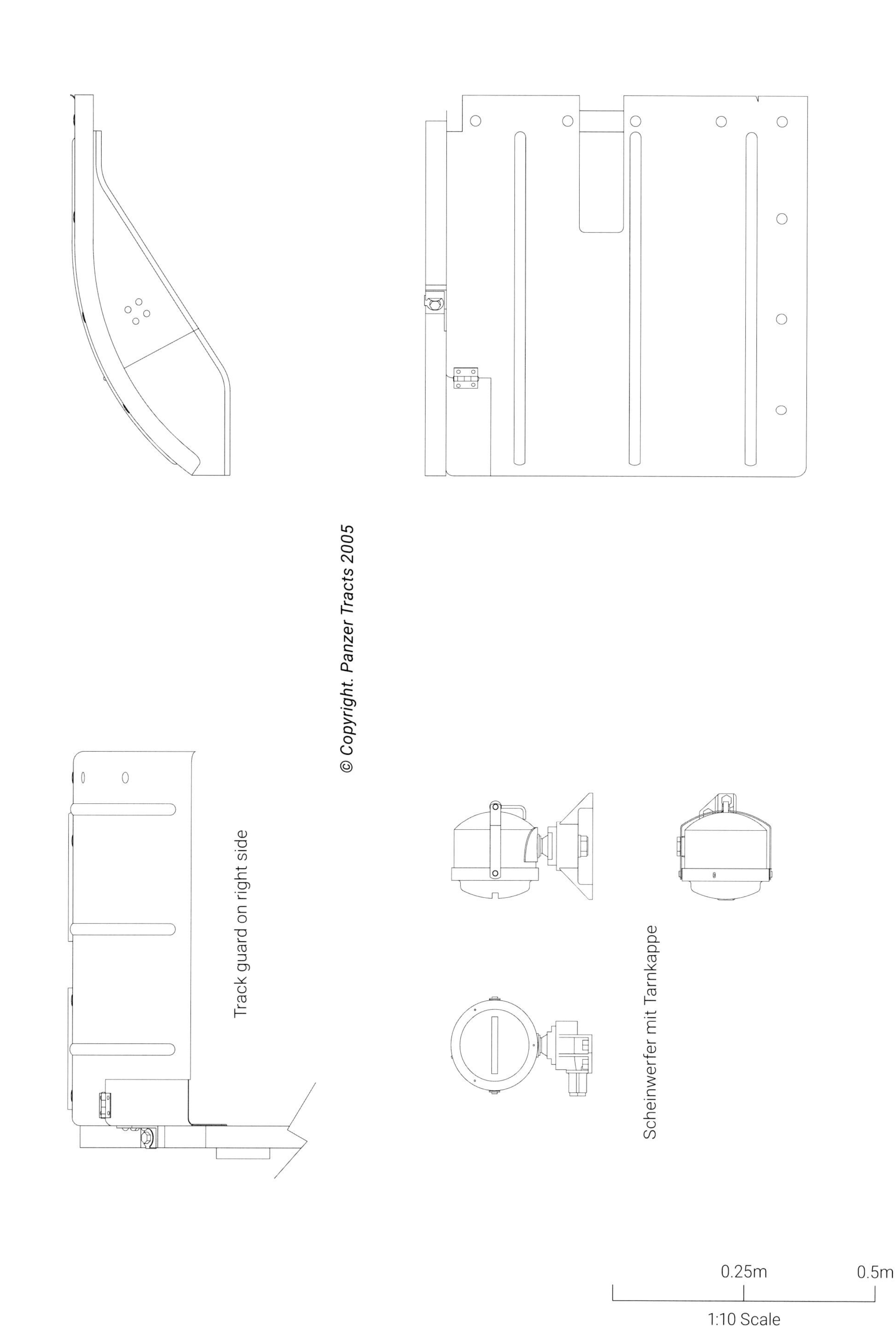
Track guard on right side
Scheinwerfer mit Tarnkappe
© Copyright. Panzer Tracts 2005
0.25m
0.5m
1:10 Scale

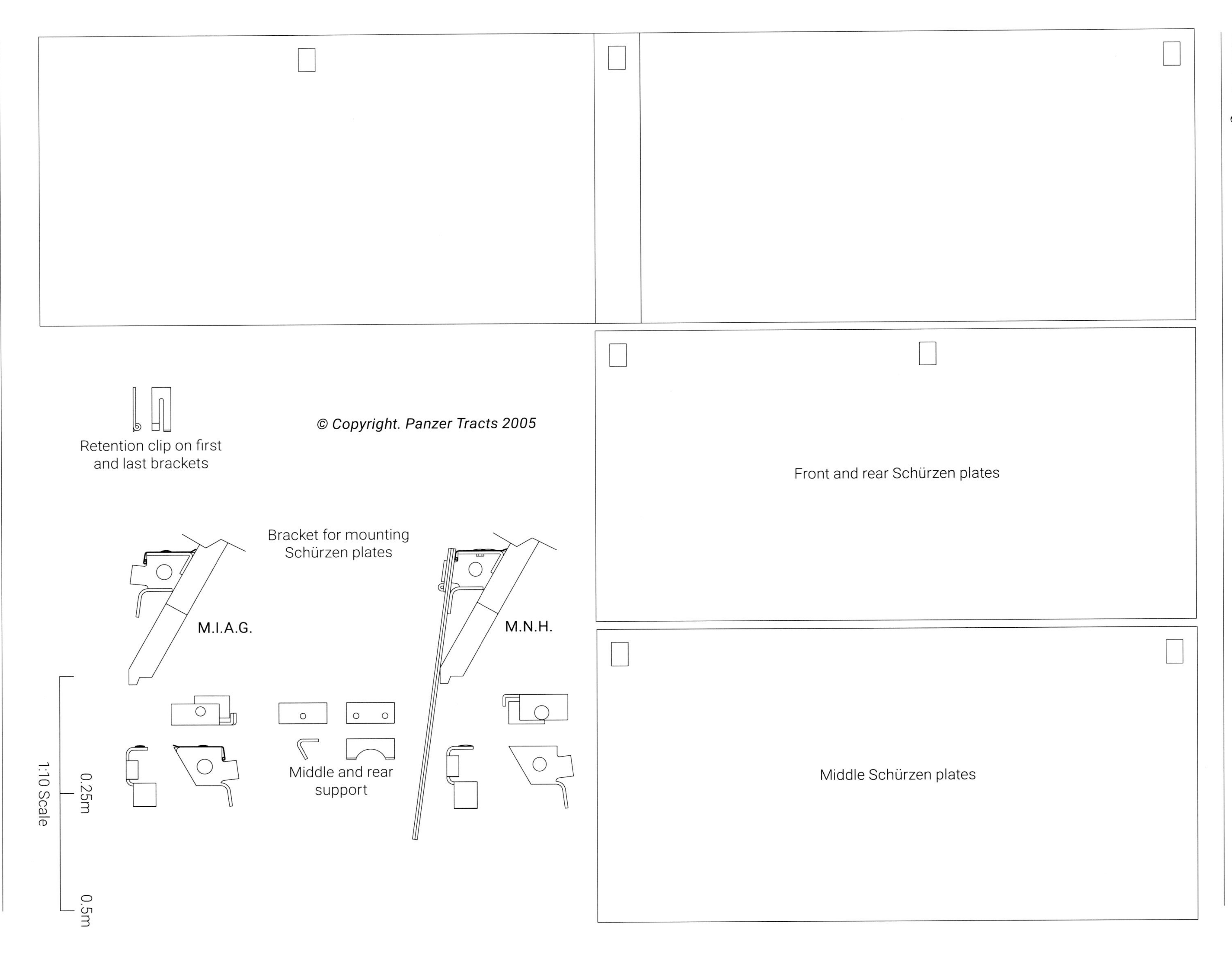

© Copyright. Panzer Tracts 2005
Retention clip on first and last brackets
Front and rear Schürzen plates
Bracket for mounting Schürzen plates
M.I.A.G.
M.N.H.
Middle and rear support
Middle Schürzen plates
1:10 Scale
0.25m
0.5m

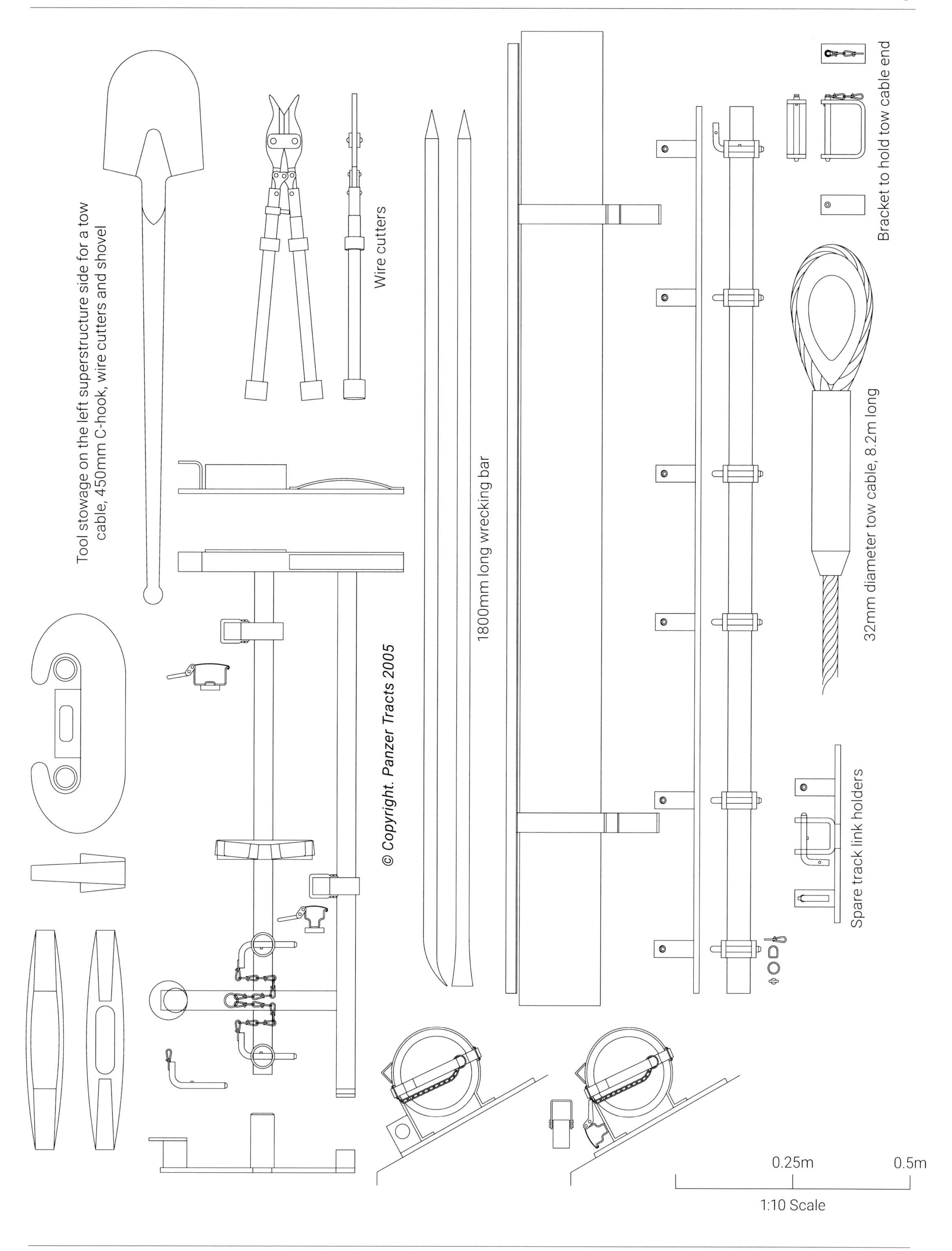
Tool stowage on the left superstructure side for a tow cable, 450mm C-hook, wire cutters and shovel
Wire cutters
© Copyright. Panzer Tracts 2005
1800mm long wrecking bar
Bracket to hold tow cable end
32mm diameter tow cable, 8.2m long
Spare track link holders
0.25m
0.5m
1:10 Scale

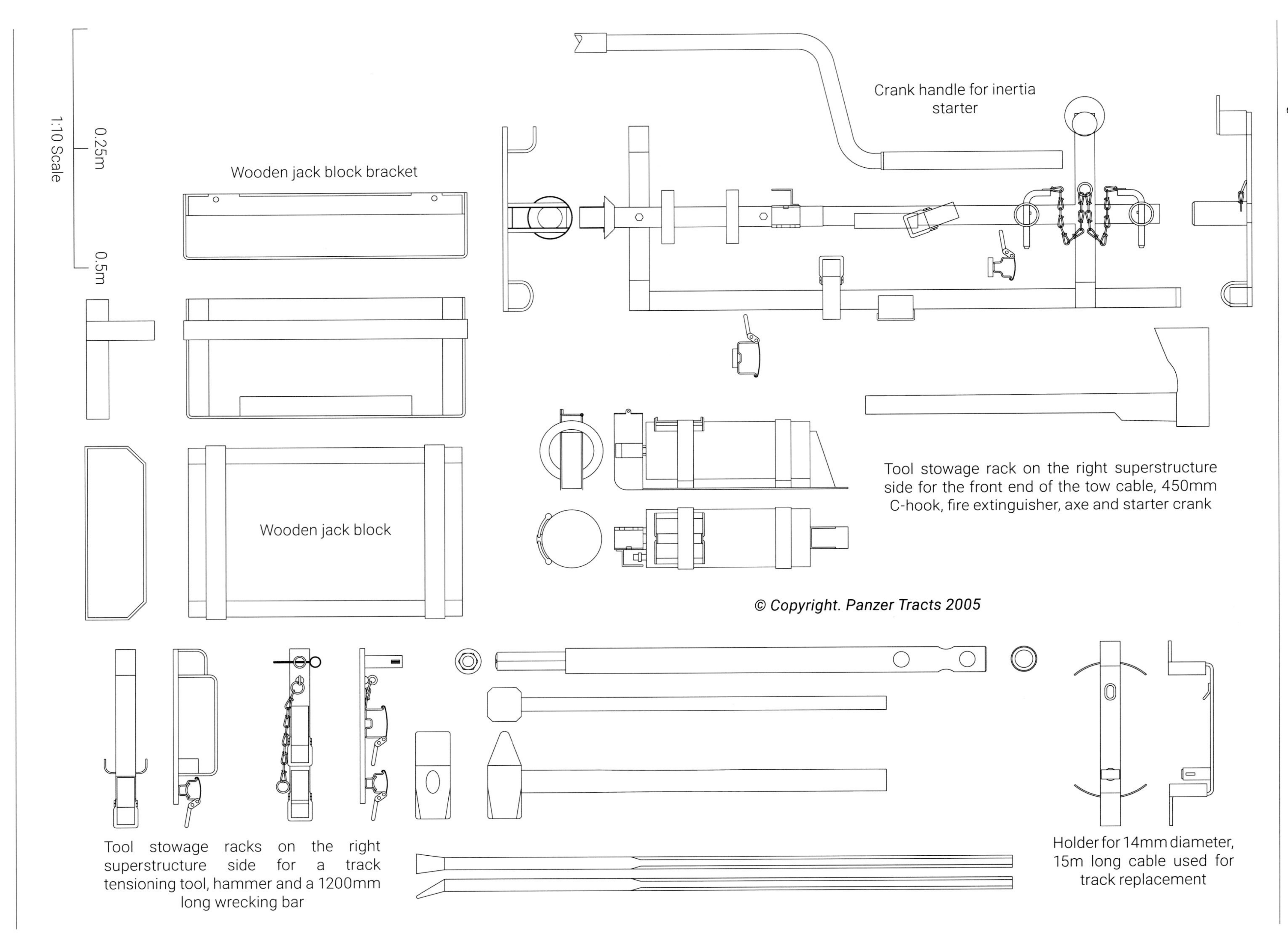
Crank handle for inertia starter
Wooden jack block bracket
0.25m
0.5m
1:10 Scale
Wooden jack block
Tool stowage rack on the right superstructure side for the front end of the tow cable, 450mm C-hook, fire extinguisher, axe and starter crank
© Copyright. Panzer Tracts 2005
Tool stowage racks on the right superstructure side for a track tensioning tool, hammer and a 1200mm long wrecking bar
Holder for 14mm diameter, 15m long cable used for track replacement

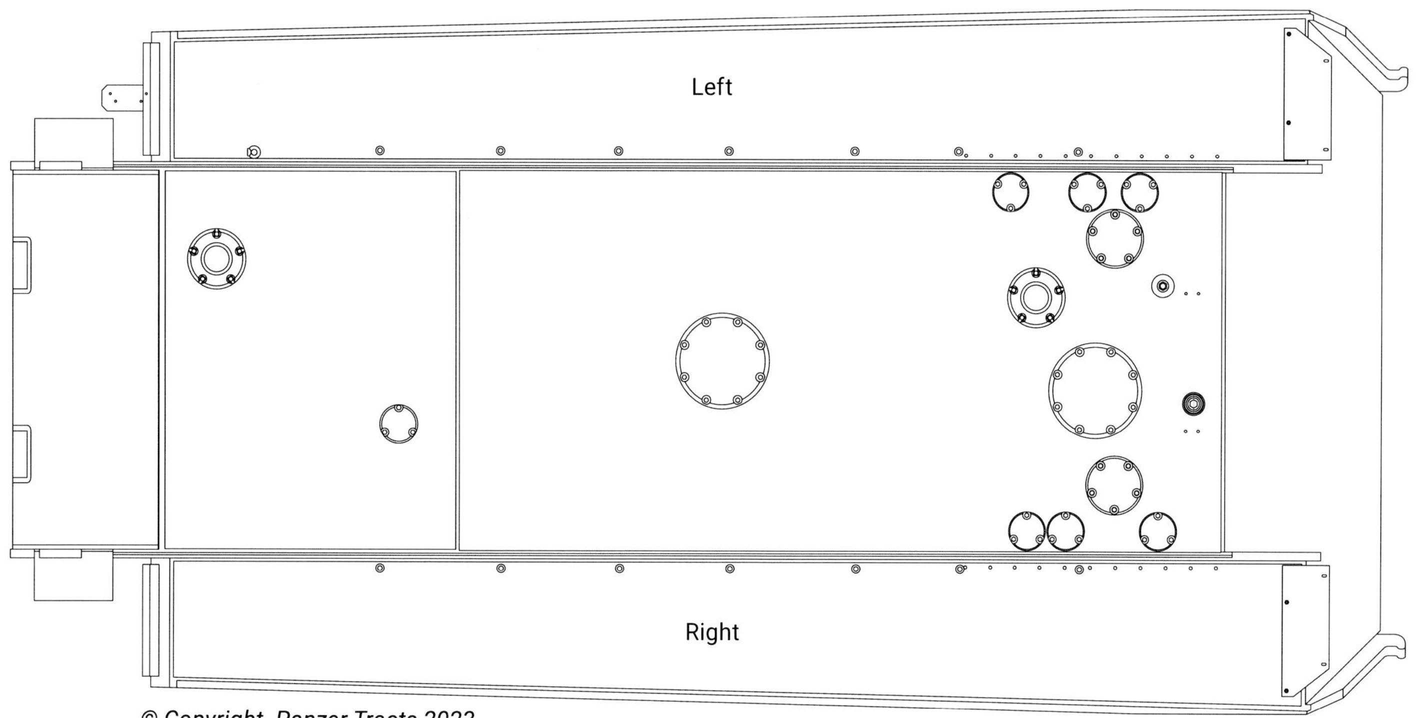

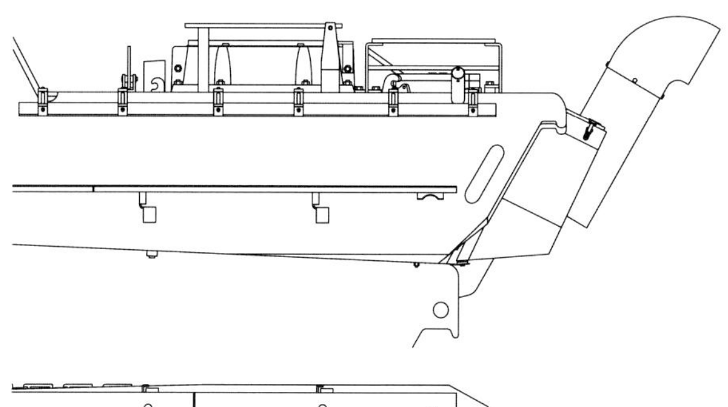

The belly for the redesigned Jagdpanther Ausf.G2 Panzerwanne (021 B 51271) was still constructed by welding a 25mm thick plate at the front fol lowed by a single 16mm thick plate at the rear. Each of the panniers was made out of a single 16mm thick plate. Two remotely operated drain ports were added to the Jagdpanther Ausf.G2 production series - one in the left front corner and a second under the engine.

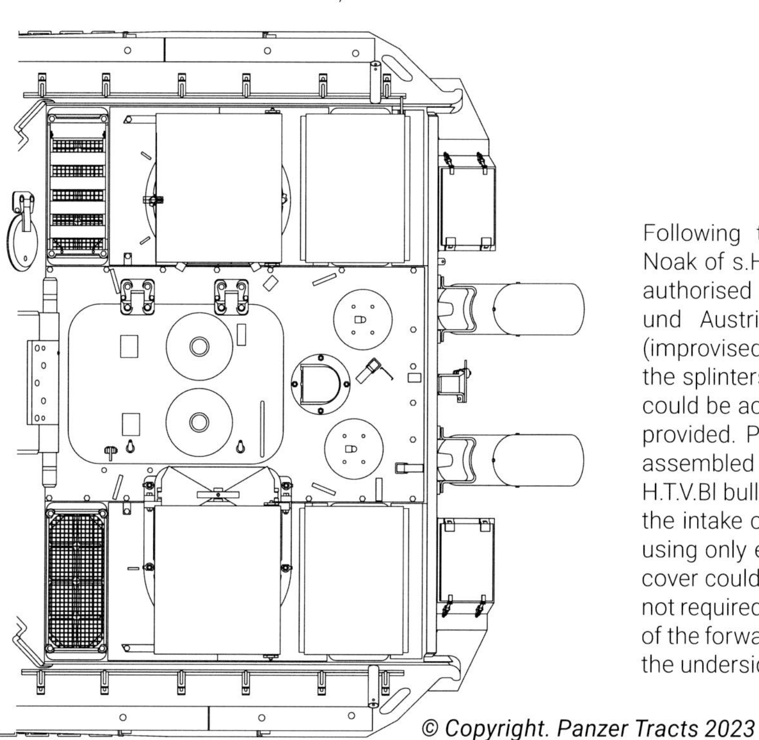

Following the demands of the troops such as Hauptmann Noak of s.H.Pz.Jg.654 in chapter 5.1 Combat Service, a H.T.V.Bl authorised a 'Behelfslösung für die beschusssichere der Luftein- und Austrittsöffnungen am Pz.Kpfwg. Panther u. Abarten' (improvised solution to protect the air intakes and outlets) from the splinters from overhead artillery bursts. A sketch of how this could be achieved by the units using spare Schürzen plates was provided. Photographic evidence of at least 15 of Jagdpanther assembled by M.I.A.G. in 1945 had an interpretation of this H.T.V.Bl bulletin applied. However, the plate used was thicker, and the intake covers longer. These additional covers were attached using only existing bolt positions on the engine deck. The outlet cover could be folded back onto the top of the inlet covers when not required. The H.T.V.Bl bulletin also specified that the open area of the forward inlets be reduced by welding small strips of plate to the underside of the grille.

1m 2m

1:35 Scale

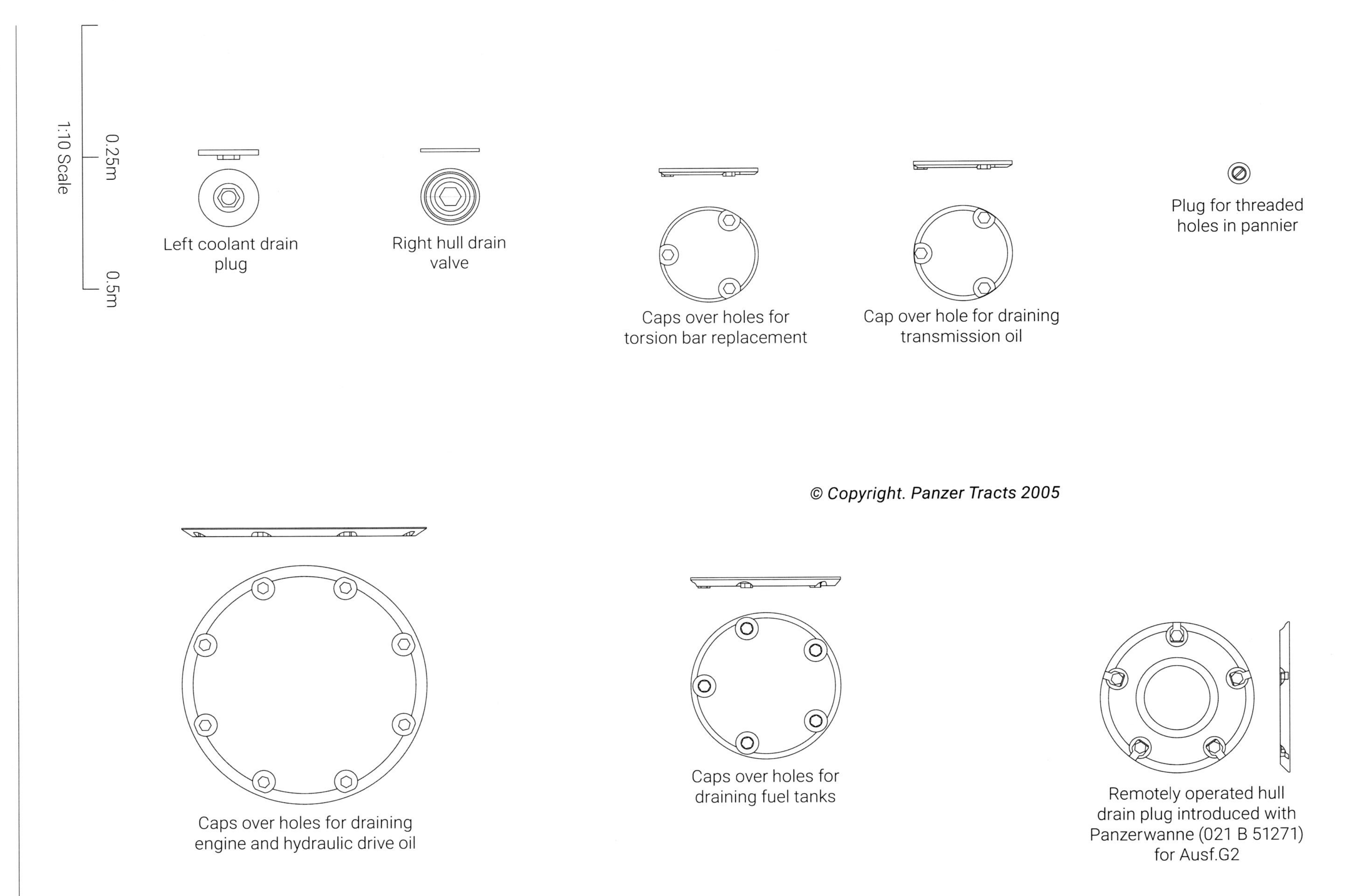

0.25m
0.5m
1:10 Scale
Left coolant drain plug
Right hull drain valve
Caps over holes for torsion bar replacement
Cap over hole for draining transmission oil
Plug for threaded holes in pannier
© Copyright. Panzer Tracts 2005
Caps over holes for draining engine and hydraulic drive oil
Caps over holes for draining fuel tanks
Remotely operated hull drain plug introduced with Panzerwanne (021 B 51271) for Ausf.G2

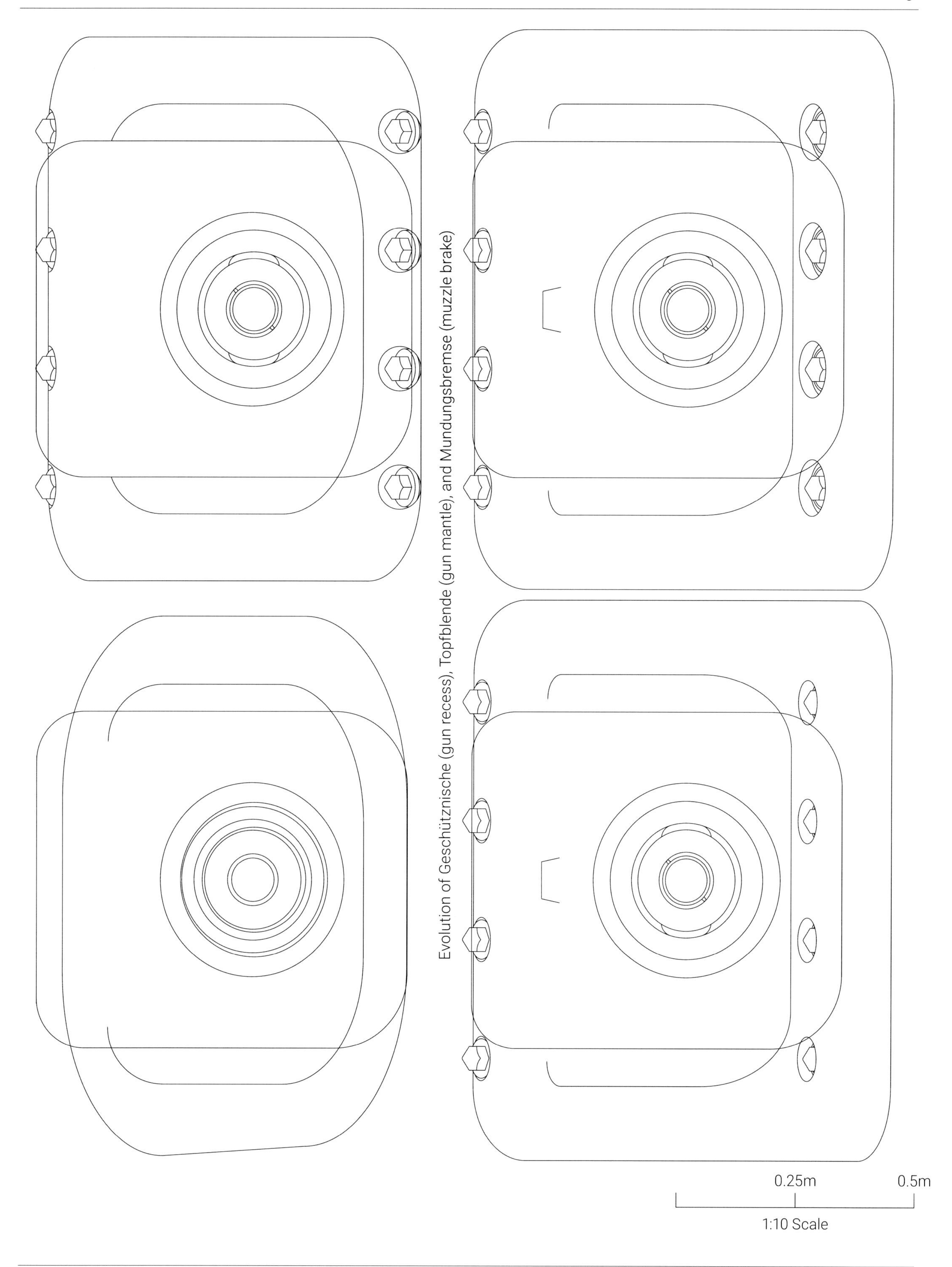
Evolution of Geschütznische (gun recess), Topfblende (gun mantle), and Mundungsbremse (muzzle brake)
0.25m
0.5m
1:10 Scale

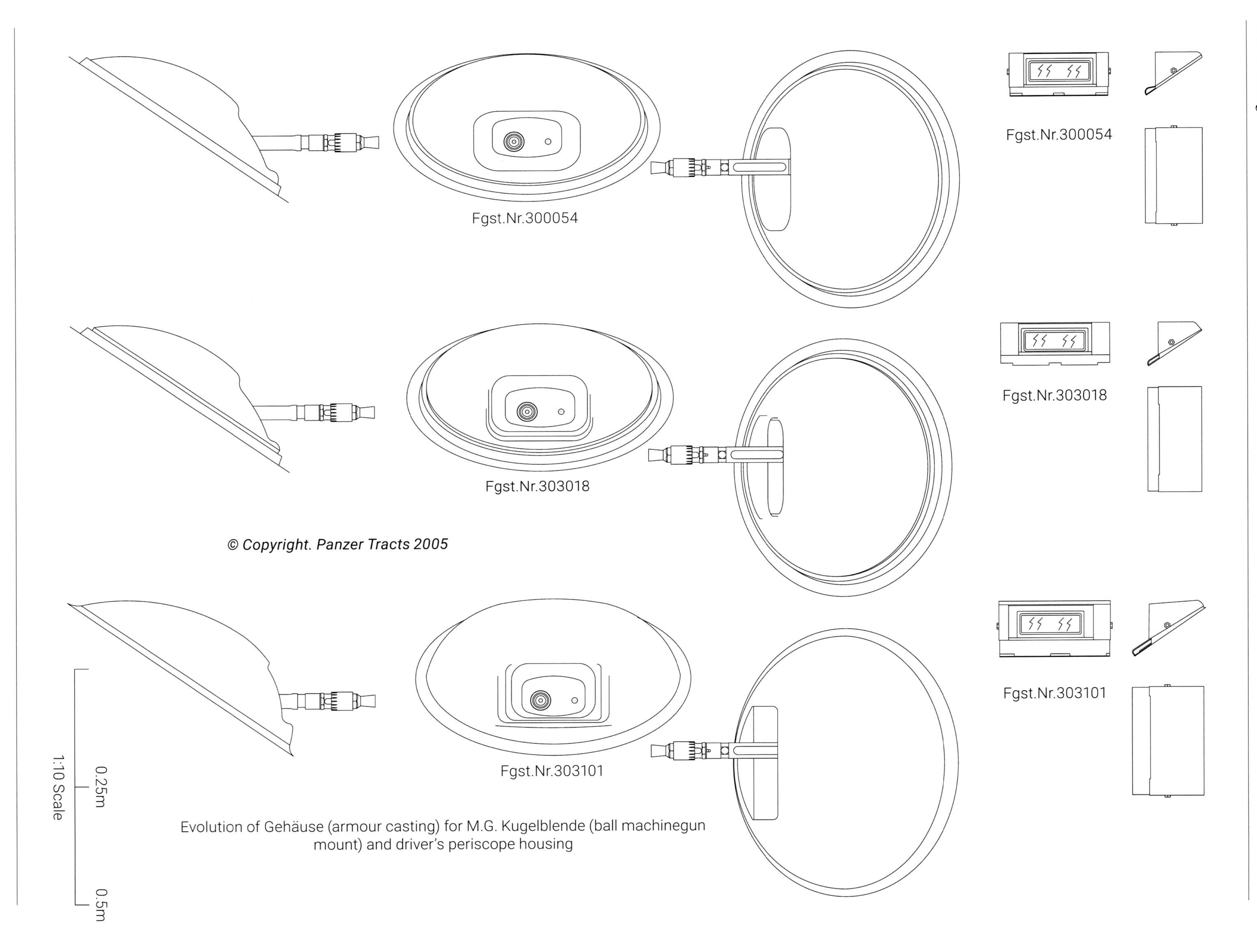

Evolution of Gehäuse (armour casting) for M.G. Kugelblende (ball machinegun mount) and driver's periscope housing

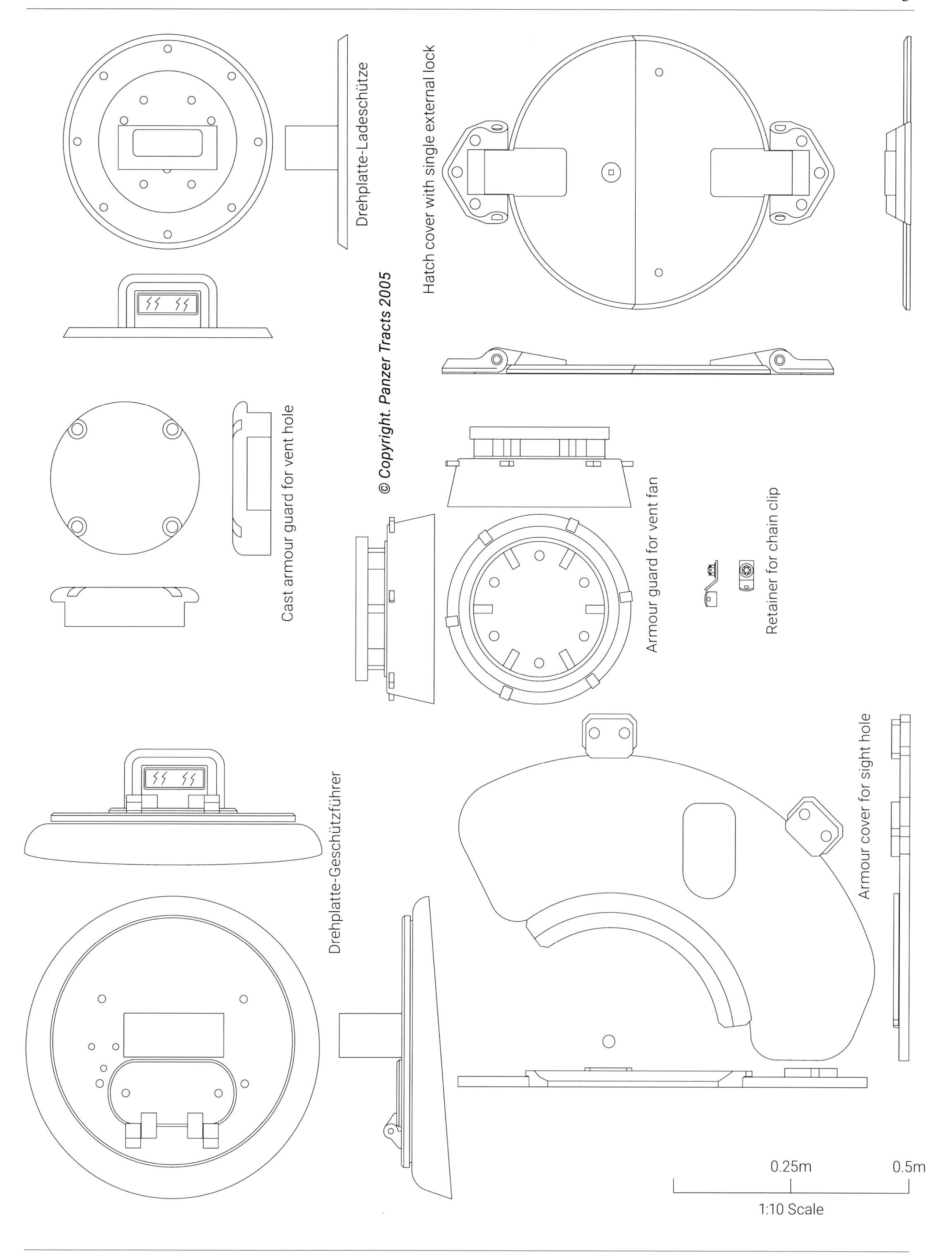
Drehplatte-Ladeschütze
Hatch cover with single external lock
© Copyright. Panzer Tracts 2005
Cast armour guard for vent hole
Armour guard for vent fan
Retainer for chain clip
Drehplatte-Geschützführer
Armour cover for sight hole
0.25m
0.5m
1:10 Scale

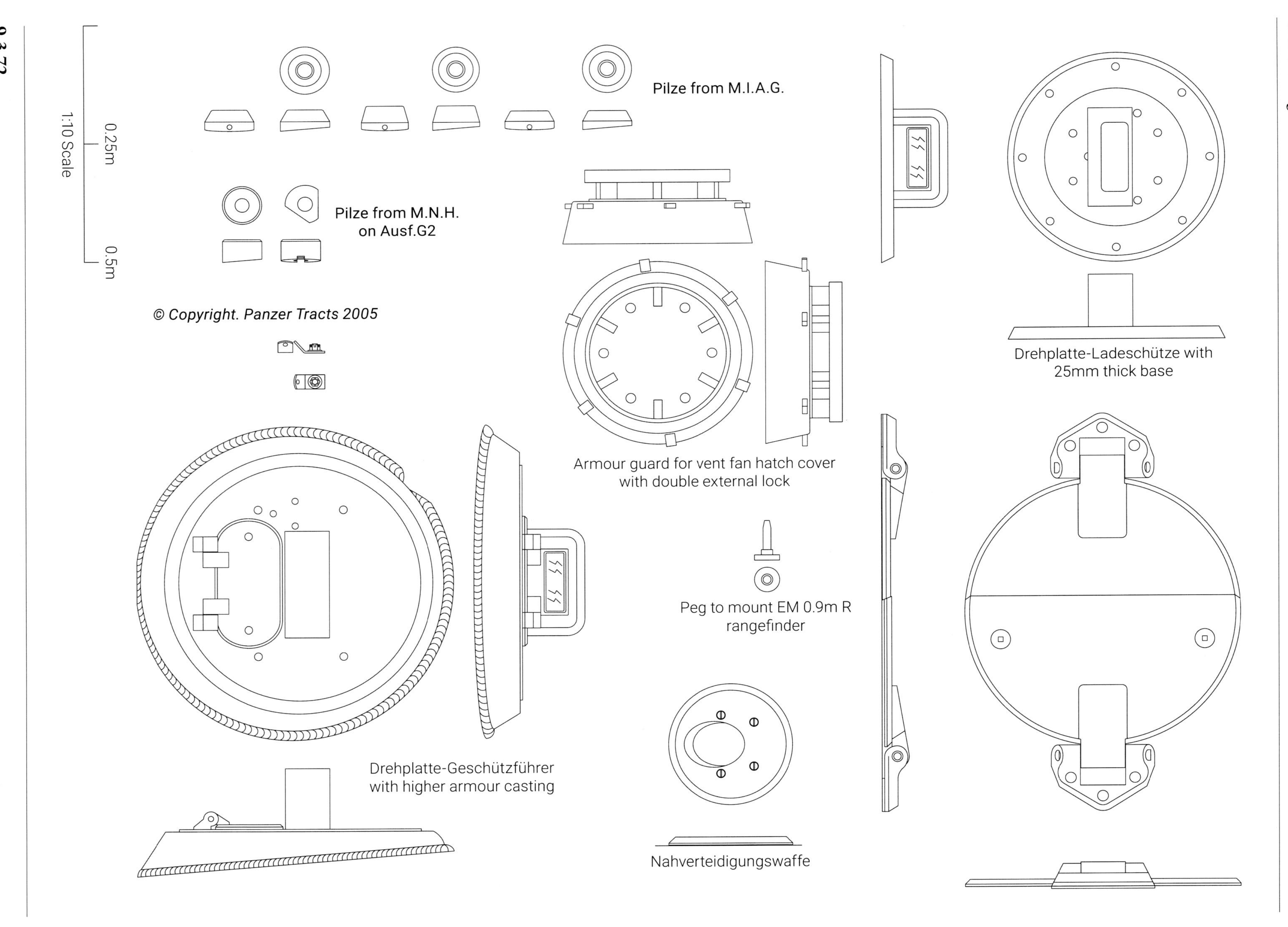
Pilze from M.I.A.G.
Pilze from M.N.H.
on Ausf.G2
© Copyright. Panzer Tracts 2005
Drehplatte-Ladeschütze with
25mm thick base
Armour guard for vent fan hatch cover
with double external lock
Peg to mount EM 0.9m R
rangefinder
Drehplatte-Geschützführer
with higher armour casting
Nahverteidigungswaffe
0.25m
0.5m
1:10 Scale

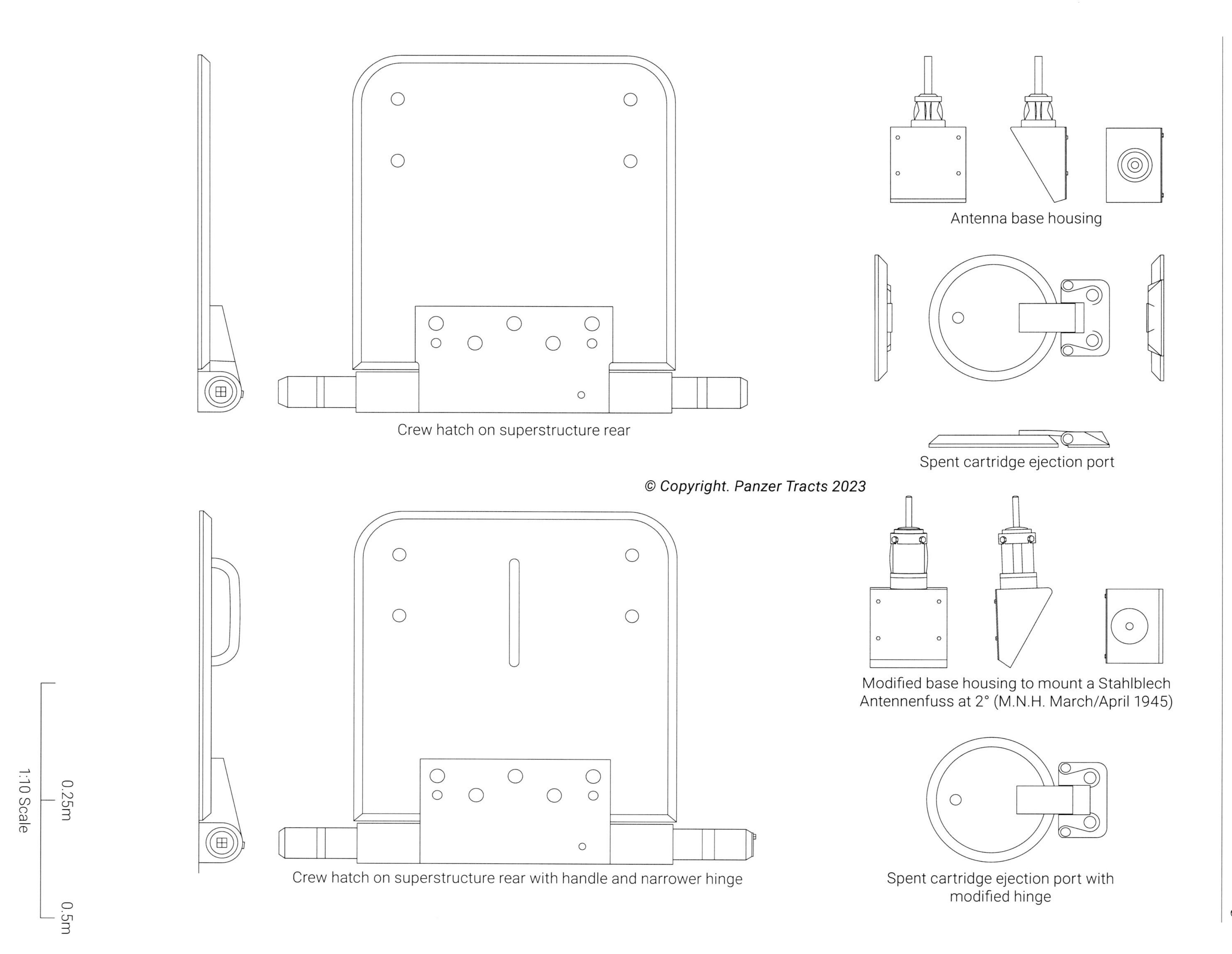
Crew hatch on superstructure rear
Antenna base housing
Spent cartridge ejection port
© Copyright. Panzer Tracts 2023
Modified base housing to mount a Stahlblech
Antennenfuss at 2° (M.N.H. March/April 1945)
Crew hatch on superstructure rear with handle and narrower hinge
Spent cartridge ejection port with
modified hinge
0.25m
0.5m
1:10 Scale

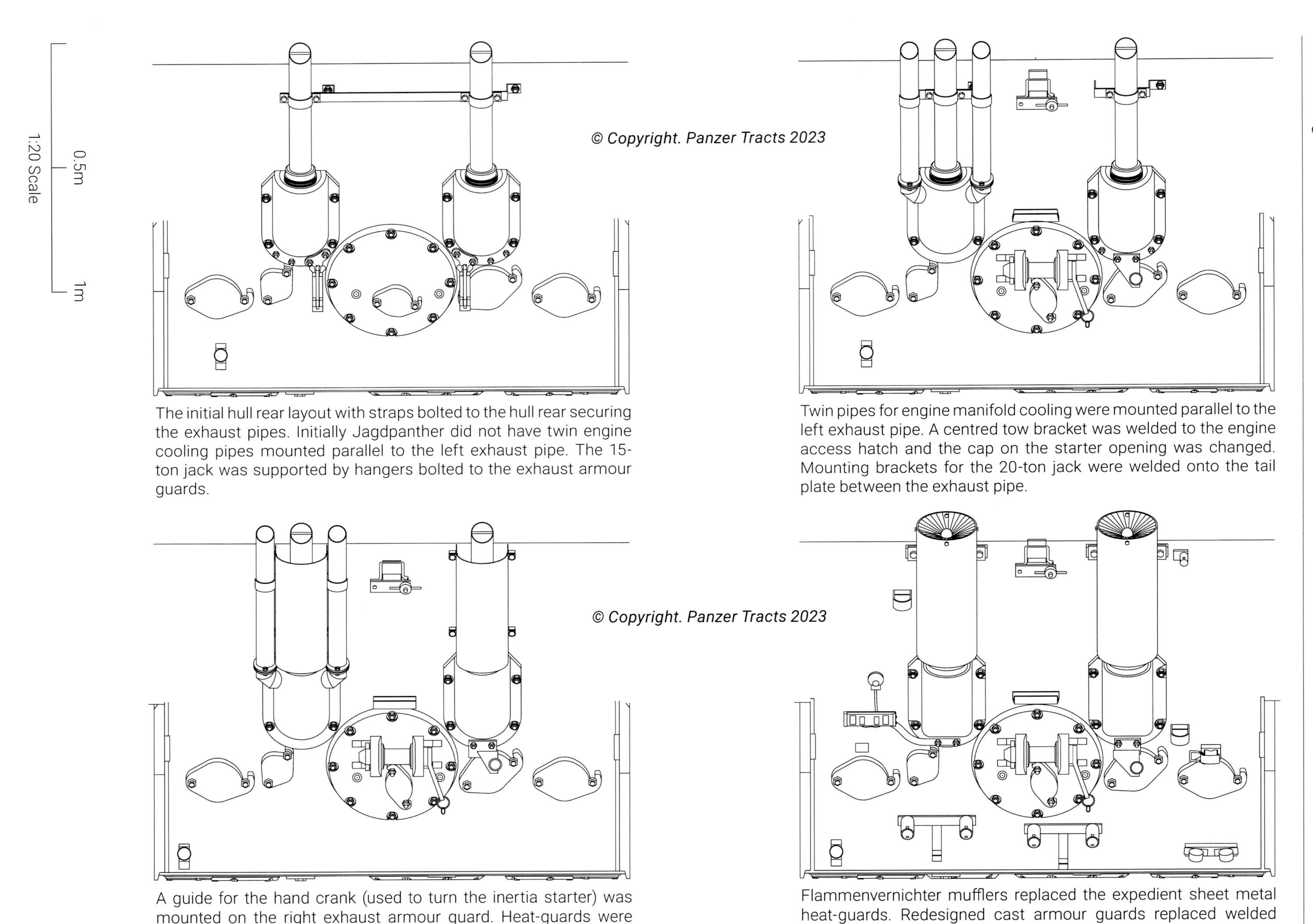

The initial hull rear layout with straps bolted to the hull rear securing the exhaust pipes. Initially Jagdpanther did not have twin engine cooling pipes mounted parallel to the left exhaust pipe. The 15-ton jack was supported by hangers bolted to the exhaust armour guards.

Twin pipes for engine manifold cooling were mounted parallel to the left exhaust pipe. A centred tow bracket was welded to the engine access hatch and the cap on the starter opening was changed. Mounting brackets for the 20-ton jack were welded onto the tail plate between the exhaust pipe.

A guide for the hand crank (used to turn the inertia starter) was mounted on the right exhaust armour guard. Heat-guards were added to cover the glowing exhaust pipes.

Flammenvernichter mufflers replaced the expedient sheet metal heat-guards. Redesigned cast armour guards replaced welded armour guards. Tool stowage was moved from the sides to the tail plate.

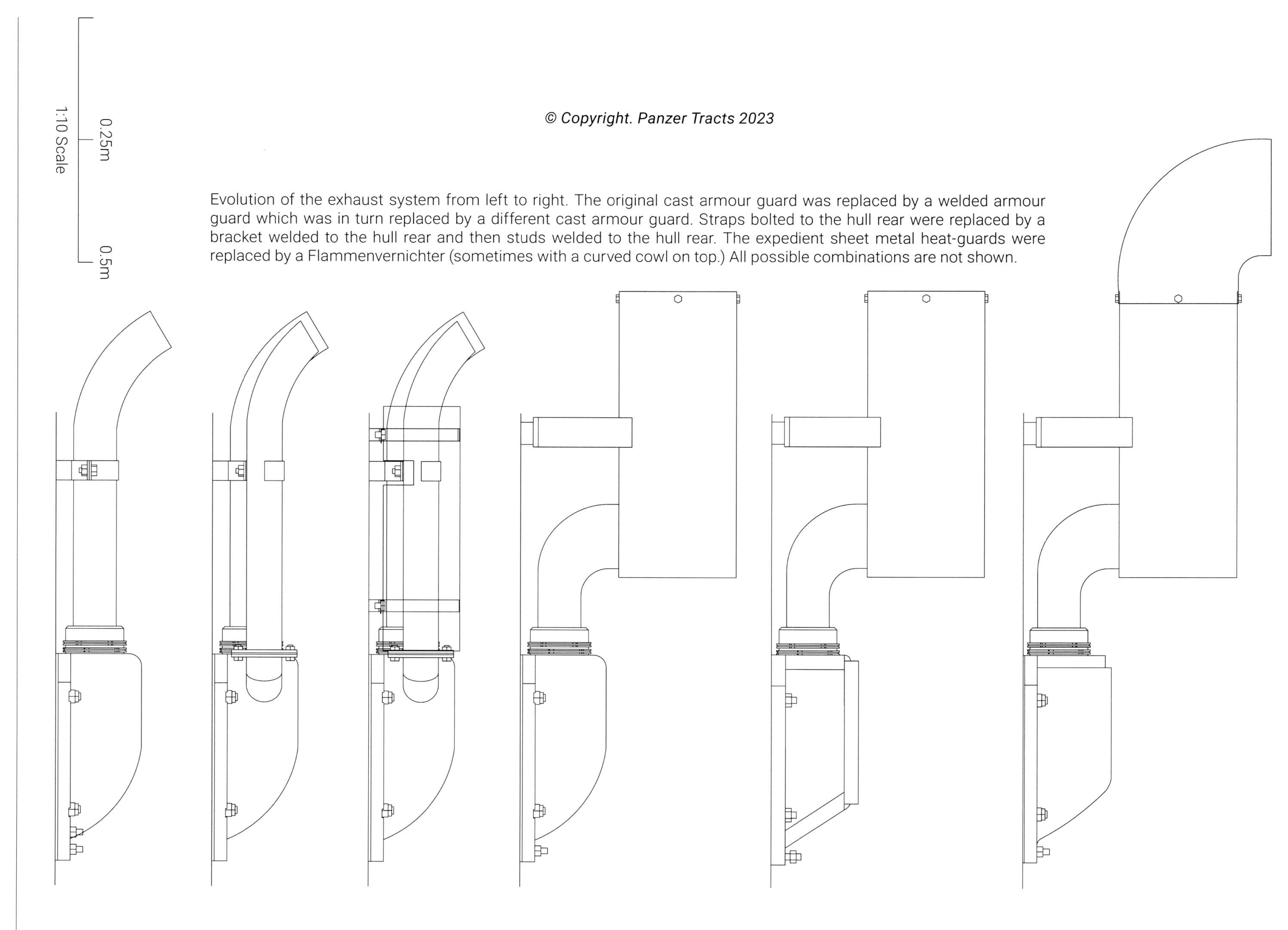

Evolution of the exhaust system from left to right. The original cast armour guard was replaced by a welded armour guard which was in turn replaced by a different cast armour guard. Straps bolted to the hull rear were replaced by a bracket welded to the hull rear and then studs welded to the hull rear. The expedient sheet metal heat-guards were replaced by a Flammenvernichter (sometimes with a curved cowl on top.) All possible combinations are not shown.

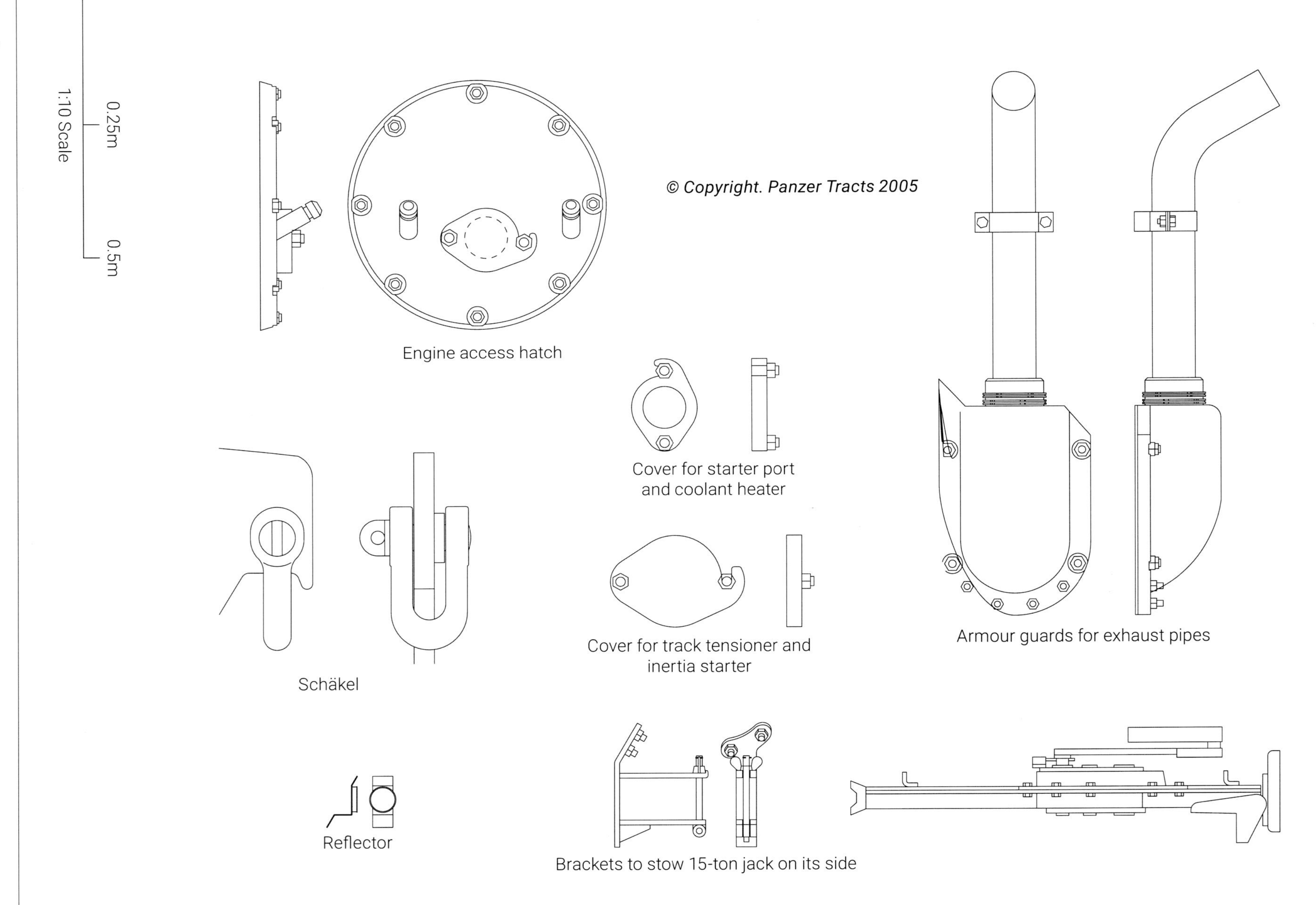
© Copyright. Panzer Tracts 2005
Engine access hatch
Cover for starter port
and coolant heater
Cover for track tensioner and
inertia starter
Armour guards for exhaust pipes
Schäkel
Reflector
Brackets to stow 15-ton jack on its side
0.25m
0.5m
1:10 Scale

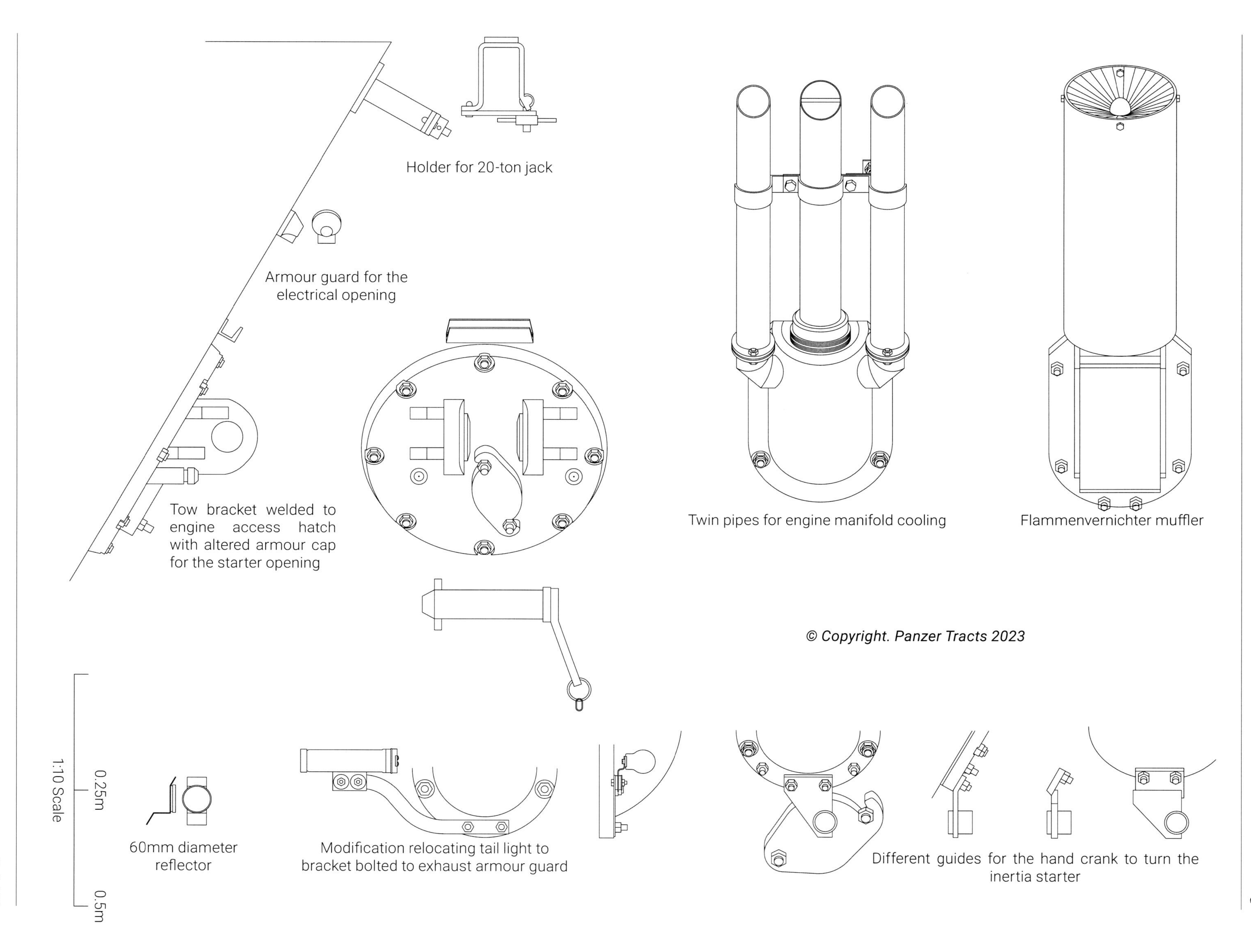
Holder for 20-ton jack
Armour guard for the electrical opening
Tow bracket welded to engine access hatch with altered armour cap for the starter opening
Twin pipes for engine manifold cooling
Flammenvernichter muffler
© Copyright. Panzer Tracts 2023
1:10 Scale
0.25m
0.5m
60mm diameter reflector
Modification relocating tail light to bracket bolted to exhaust armour guard
Different guides for the hand crank to turn the inertia starter

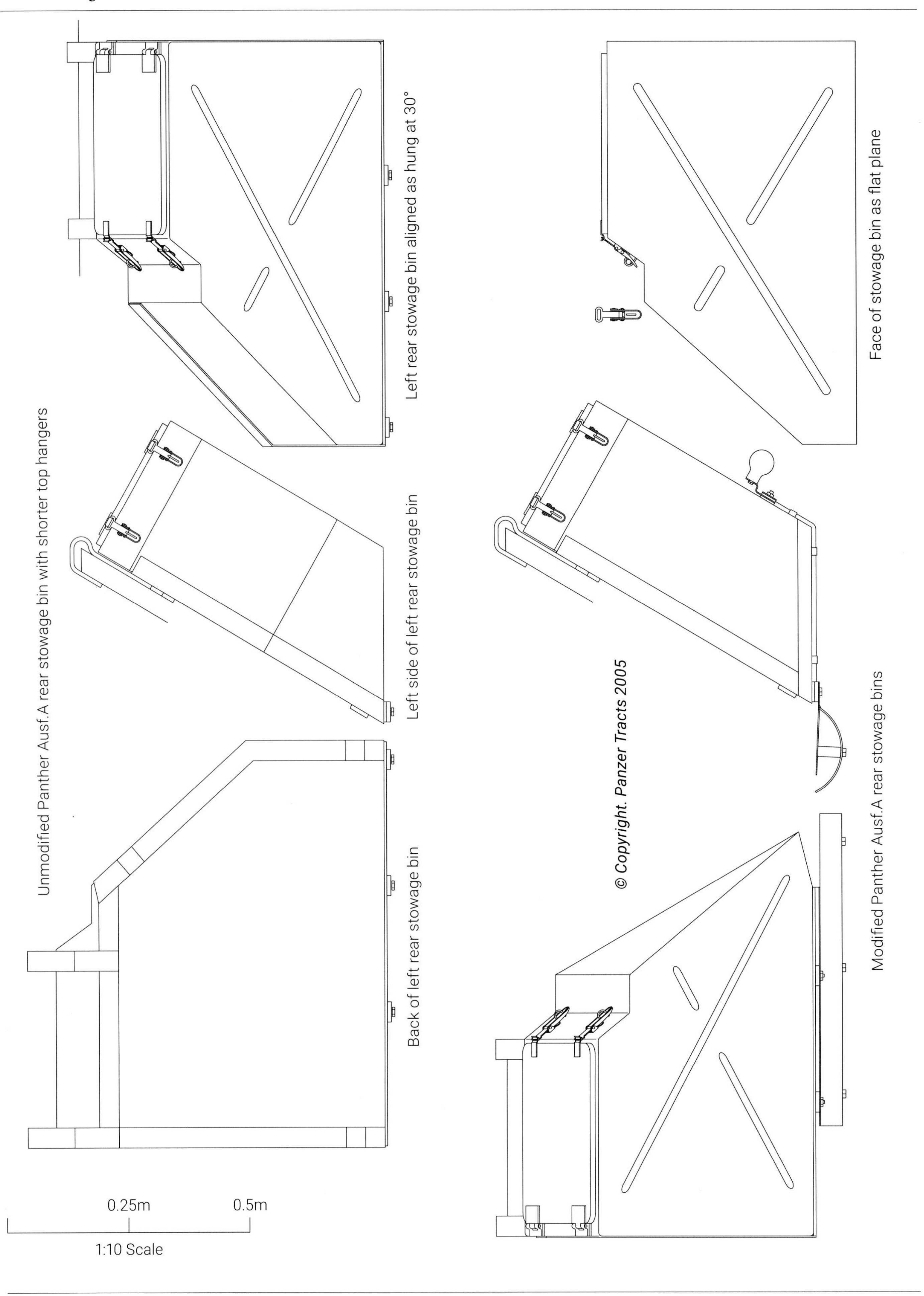
Unmodified Panther Ausf.A rear stowage bin with shorter top hangers
Left rear stowage bin aligned as hung at 30°
Left side of left rear stowage bin
Back of left rear stowage bin
Face of stowage bin as flat plane
Modified Panther Ausf.A rear stowage bins
© Copyright. Panzer Tracts 2005
0.25m
0.5m
1:10 Scale

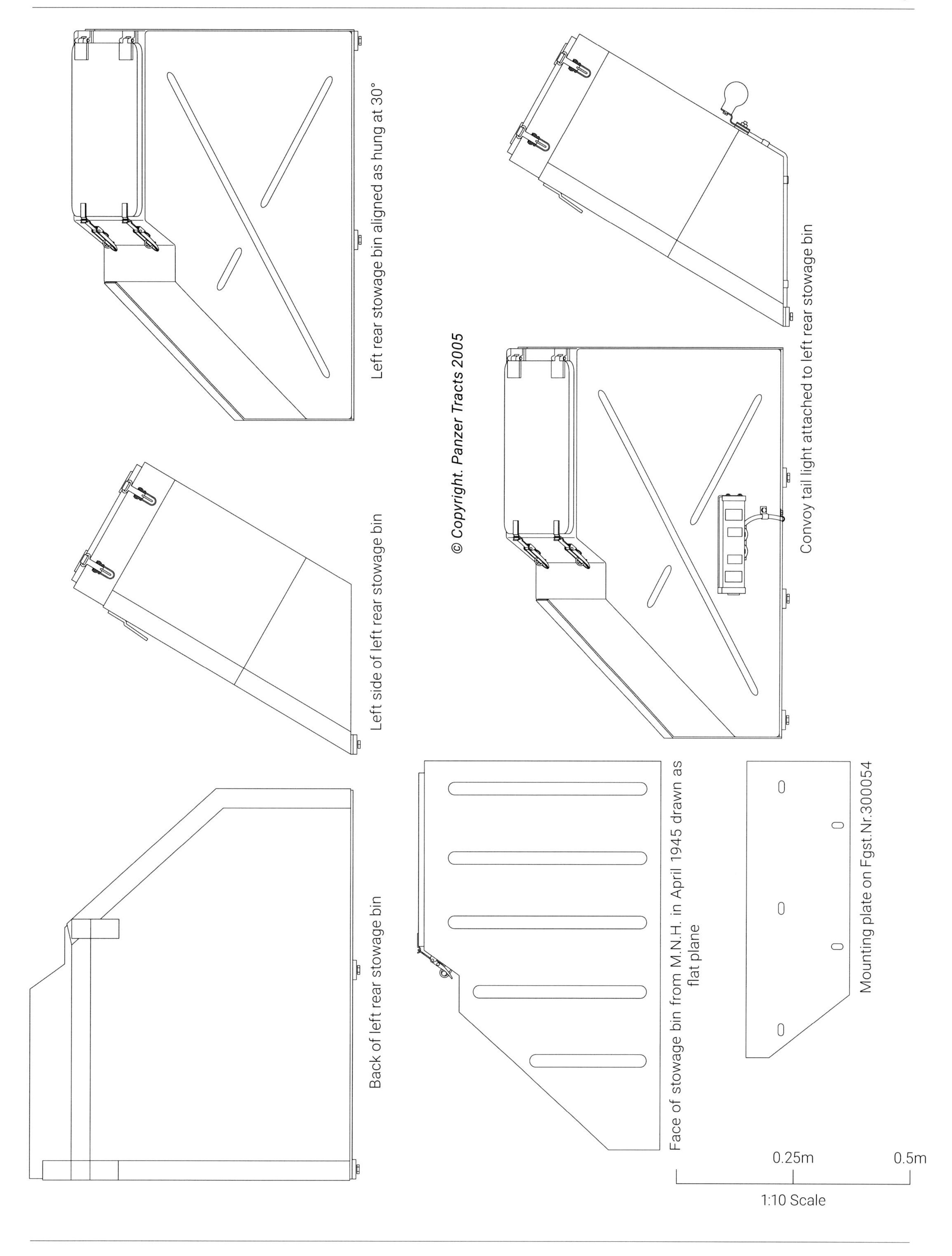
Left rear stowage bin aligned as hung at 30°
Left side of left rear stowage bin
Back of left rear stowage bin
© Copyright. Panzer Tracts 2005
Convoy tail light attached to left rear stowage bin
Face of stowage bin from M.N.H. in April 1945 drawn as flat plane
Mounting plate on Fgst.Nr.300054
0.25m
0.5m
1:10 Scale

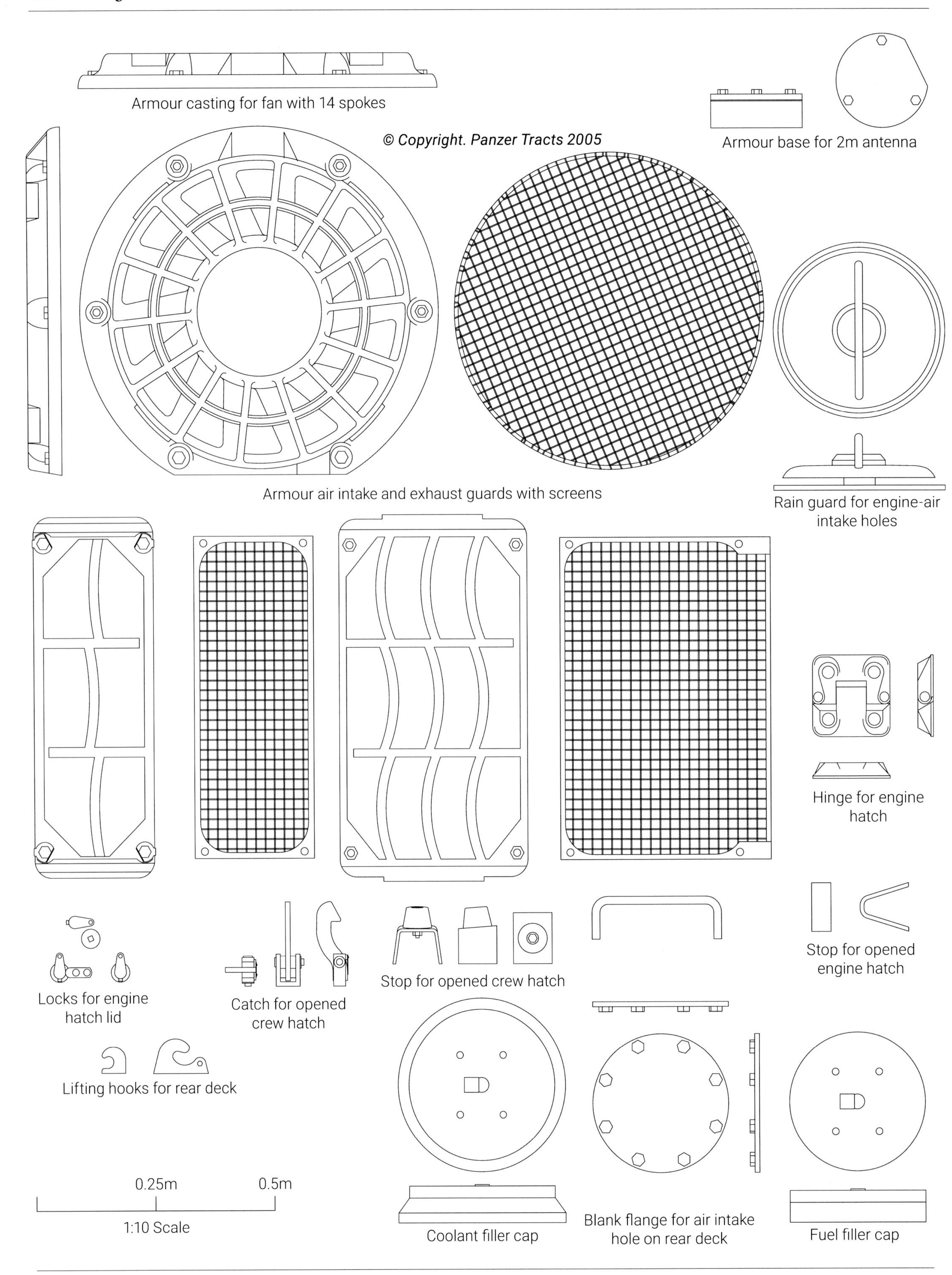
Armour casting for fan with 14 spokes
Armour base for 2m antenna
© Copyright. Panzer Tracts 2005
Armour air intake and exhaust guards with screens
Rain guard for engine-air intake holes
Hinge for engine hatch
Stop for opened engine hatch
Locks for engine hatch lid
Catch for opened crew hatch
Stop for opened crew hatch
Lifting hooks for rear deck
0.25m
0.5m
1:10 Scale
Coolant filler cap
Blank flange for air intake hole on rear deck
Fuel filler cap

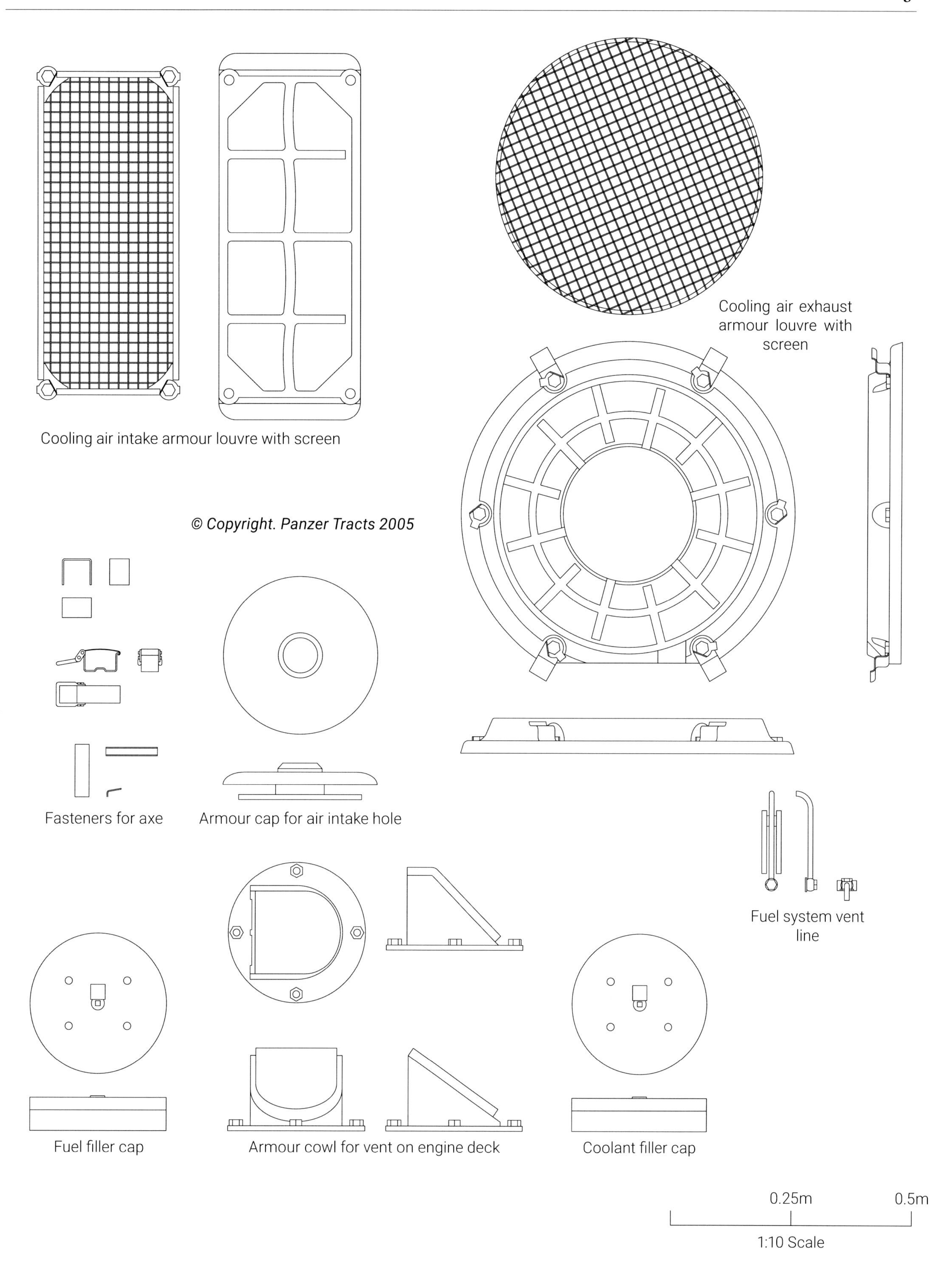
Cooling air exhaust armour louvre with screen
Cooling air intake armour louvre with screen
© Copyright. Panzer Tracts 2005
Fasteners for axe
Armour cap for air intake hole
Fuel system vent line
Fuel filler cap
Armour cowl for vent on engine deck
Coolant filler cap
0.25m
0.5m
1:10 Scale

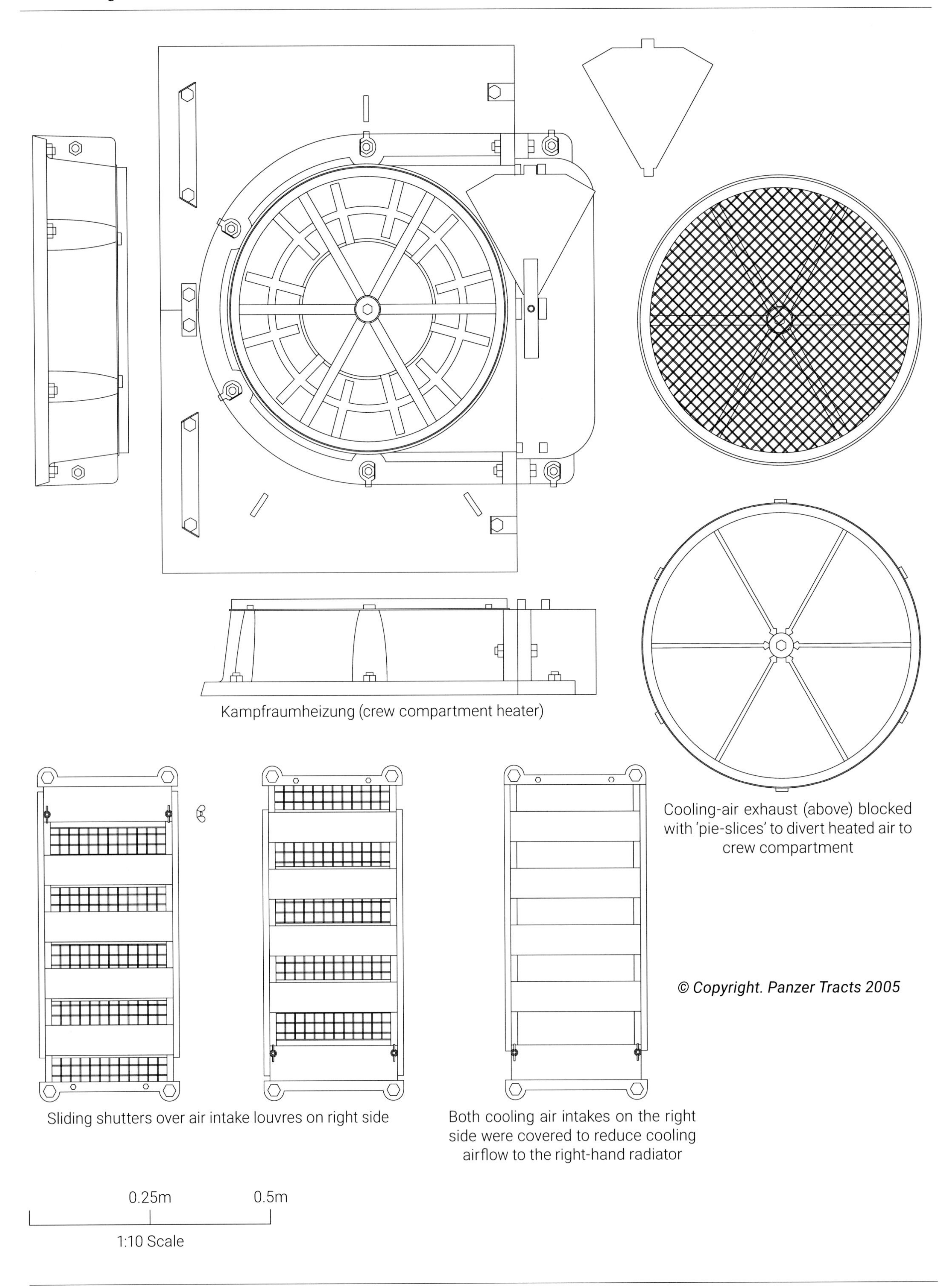

Kampfraumheizung (crew compartment heater)

Cooling-air exhaust (above) blocked with 'pie-slices' to divert heated air to crew compartment

Sliding shutters over air intake louvres on right side

Both cooling air intakes on the right side were covered to reduce cooling airflow to the right-hand radiator

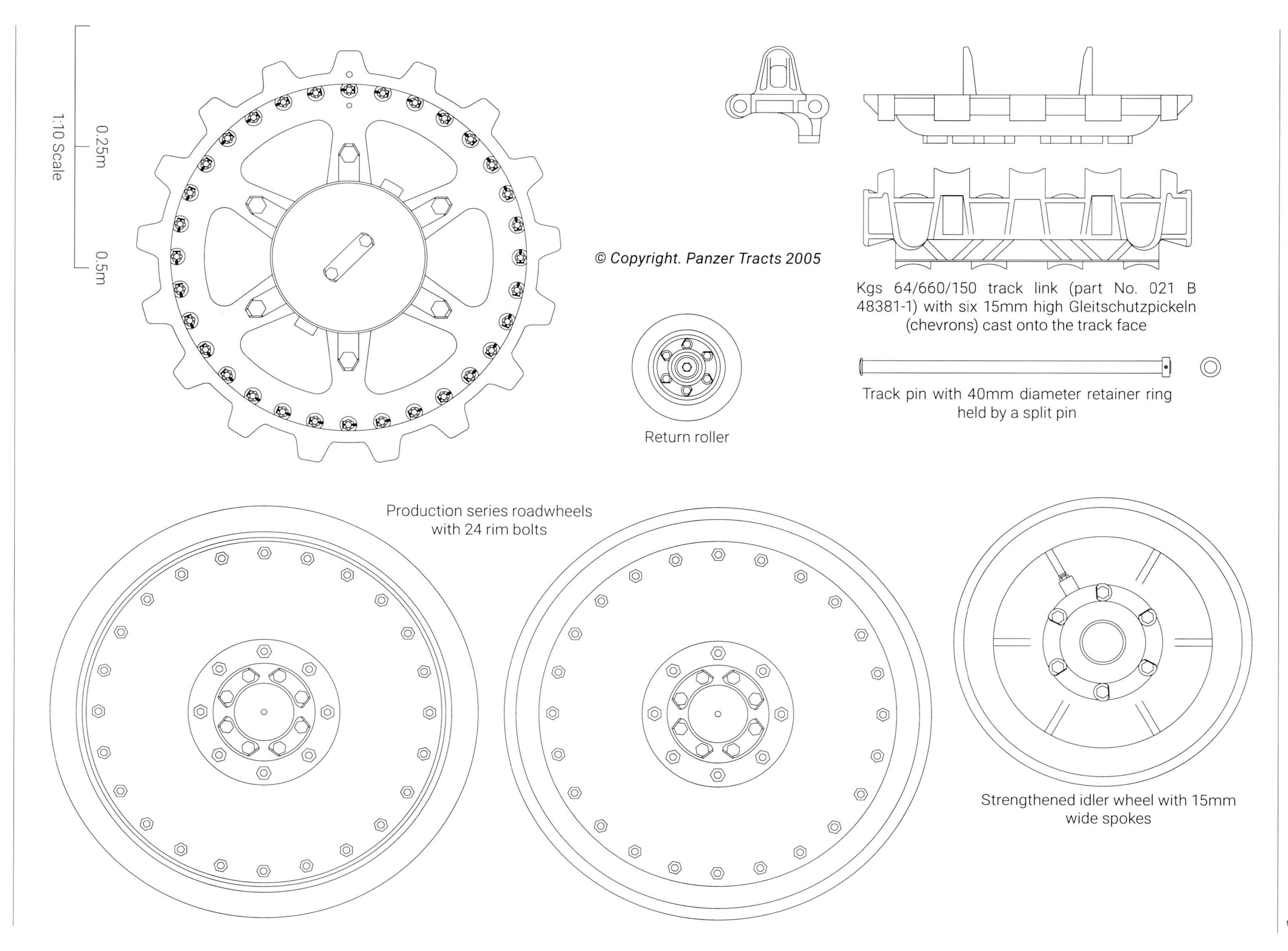

0.25m
0.5m
1:10 Scale
© Copyright. Panzer Tracts 2005
Kgs 64/660/150 track link (part No. 021 B 48381-1) with six 15mm high Gleitschutzpickeln (chevrons) cast onto the track face
Track pin with 40mm diameter retainer ring held by a split pin
Return roller
Production series roadwheels with 24 rim bolts
Strengthened idler wheel with 15mm wide spokes

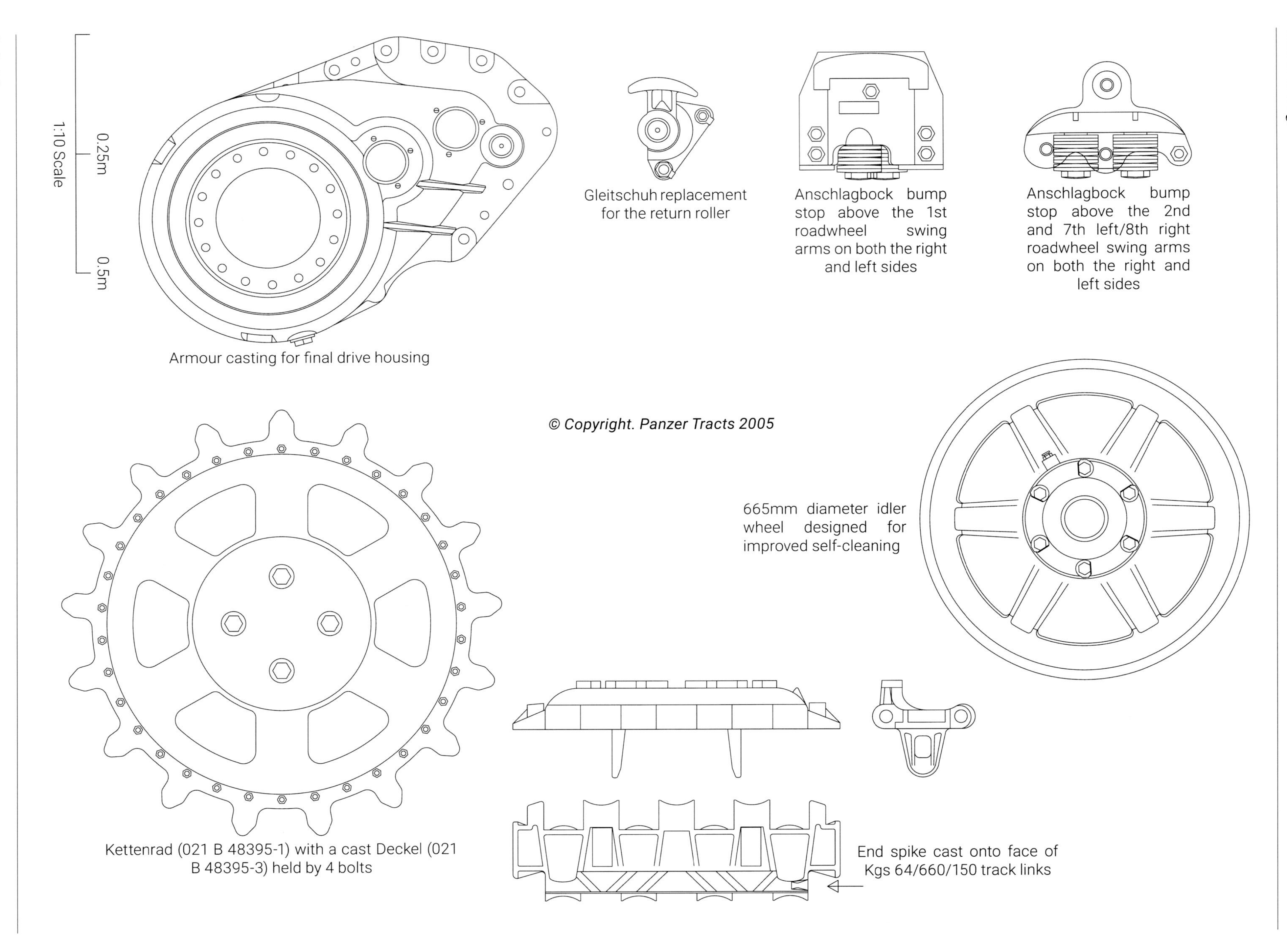
0.25m
0.5m
1:10 Scale
Gleitschuh replacement for the return roller
Anschlagbock bump stop above the 1st roadwheel swing arms on both the right and left sides
Anschlagbock bump stop above the 2nd and 7th left/8th right roadwheel swing arms on both the right and left sides
Armour casting for final drive housing
© Copyright. Panzer Tracts 2005
665mm diameter idler wheel designed for improved self-cleaning
Kettenrad (021 B 48395-1) with a cast Deckel (021 B 48395-3) held by 4 bolts
End spike cast onto face of Kgs 64/660/150 track links

5. Organisation & Tactics

Guidelines for the tactical employment of the Jagdpanther were published in the following Merkblatt 76a/20 dated 14 June 1944, entitled Vorläfige Richtlinien für den Einsatz der schweren Panzerjäger V 'Jagdpanther'.

1. *The Jagdpanther is a schwere Panzerjäger. It is a Schwerpunktwaffe (weapon to be used against primary targets) for the higher command to decimate enemy tank attacks. Jagdpanther are concentrated in schweren Panzerjäger-Abteilungen (Jagdpanther) as Heerestruppe.*
2. *With its 8.8cm s.Pak (L/71) it can destroy all previously encountered enemy tanks at long range. Cross-country mobility and armour allow the Jagdpanther to use offensive tactics in attacking enemy tanks in order to pull our own attack forward.*
3. *The lack of all-round firing capability, limited close defence potential, and restricted vision prevent the Jagdpanther from being employed as a Panzer and make it necessary to guard it with infantry or tanks.*
4. *Employment of the concentrated Abteilung is the first prerequisite for decisive success. If the Jagdpanther must be employed in company strength, they should only be attached to divisions or higher commands. Regiments and battalions will use them for combined operations. Before assigning a mission, listen to the Jagdpanther unit commander. In all cases he remains responsible for conducting the operation. Maintenance of separately employed companies is to be ensured by the Abteilung. Employing individual Züge (platoons) is correct only in combating fixed emplacements and in close terrain. Employment of single Jagdpanther is forbidden!*
5. *In reinforcing other anti-tank weapons, the Jagdpanther are to be sent in against the main point of the enemy tank attack when his direction of attack is known. The Jagdpanther are to be thrown into the battle as a concentrated unit.*
6. *The Jagdpanther is not a Stellungs-Pak (emplaced anti-tank gun). It is unsuitable for guarding and security tasks.*
7. *The Jagdpanther is not a self-propelled artillery piece. Firing Sprenggranaten (high-explosive shells) against unarmoured targets is correct only when (1) no enemy tanks appear, (2) other heavy weapons are not available or are disabled, (3) the ammunition supply is sufficient.*
8. *Jagdpanther are to be pulled out of the front after fulfilling their combat mission. This gives them an opportunity for maintenance and restoring combat readiness. Combat readiness of the Jagdpanther depends on regular supply.*
9. *Utilise the long range of the gun by opening fire early (at 2500 metres) when engaging tanks, especially in superior numbers.*
10. *When the Jagdpanther are in hidden positions that are not spotted by the opponent, let the enemy tanks advance into their fire front. Open fire at short range for its surprise effect. Strive for concentrated fire.*
11. *The firefight should be conducted by fully utilizing mobility. Frequent position changes and firing from unexpected directions increase the effectiveness.*
12. *The enemy tank attack can be pinned down by fire from part of the Jagdpanther, while the mass of the enemy tanks are attacked and destroyed out of the flanks or rear.*
13. *The tasks for Jagdpanther within a Panzer attack are: to support the first wave by engaging the heavy and heaviest tanks, tie down enemy tanks frontally so that the Panzer attack can strike the flanks or rear, and defend one or both flanks of the Panzer attack.*
14. *In an Infanterie attack the Jagdpanther are to accompany the infantry directly behind the foremost soldiers. Their main task is to eliminate enemy tanks in the front and flanks. As long as no enemy tanks appear, targets that threaten the success of the infantry attack can be eliminated by machinegun fire and Sprenggranaten.*
15. *During attacks on fixed emplacements, the Jagdpanther support the advance of the assault troops by effectively firing at embrasures.*
16. *When pursuing a retreating enemy, the Jagdpanther along with other mobile units should strike ruthlessly. Fuel and ammunition supply is to be secured in time.*
17. *On the defensive the Jagdpanther are to be held in readiness behind frontline sectors that are especially threatened with enemy tank attack. Approach routes, assembly areas, and firing positions should be scouted and prepared in advance. Scattering piecemeal along a wide front takes away the advantage of the striking power of this high value weapon and makes resupply and command more difficult. Digging Jagdpanther into the main battle line is forbidden! Tanks that have penetrated into our positions are to be destroyed following the guidelines in paragraphs 9 through 12 above.*
18. *When breaking off the action and retreating, Jagdpanther are intended to be employed utilizing mobile tactics in the open zone. Favourable firing positions are to be scouted in time by exploiting available terrain. Firing positions are to be selected so that the Jagdpanther can quickly back away into cover. Because they lack a traversing turret*

and are difficult to retrieve, Jagdpanther are not suitable for direct support. of rear guards. Close cooperation with Grenadieren is necessary.

19. *During battles in woods and towns the Jagdpanther provide supporting fire until our own unit breaks into the position. They are minimally suitable for fighting within woods and towns, because their tactical mobility cannot be sufficiently exploited and the long gun often prevents turning movements of the Jagdpanther. Sufficient infantry escort is to be ensured in all cases.*
20. *At night, after thoroughly scouting and briefing, Jagdpanther in close contact with other weapons can be sent on attacks with limited objectives.*

Note: It is significant that in the technical data section of this manual, the maximum speed is given as 30 km/hr. It is not known whether this was an administrative limit intended to reduce mechanical breakdowns or a mistake from carrying over a number from a preliminary design There are other mistakes in this data table, including that the firing height given as 1.850 metres and fording depth at 1.55 metres - both numbers were correct for the preliminary but not the final design actually produced. Only 52 of the 60 rounds were actually stowed in racks; the other 8 were to be stowed in crates at the right and left rear corners on the floor.

A schweren Panzerjäger-Abteilung (Jagdpanther) consisted of an Abteilungstab (headquarters) with 3 Jagdpanther; Stabskompanie with Nachrichtenzug (signals), Pionierzug (combat engineers), and Fliegerabwehrzug (anti-aircraft); three Panzerjäger-Kompanien each with 14 Jagdpanther (2 in Kp.-Trupp and 4 in each of three Zuegen); Versorgunskompanie (supply); and Werkstattzug (maintenance).

The Stabskompanie einer schwerer Panzerjäger-Abteilung 'Panther' was to be organised in accordance with K.St.N.1154a(fG) dated 1Mar44 with 3 Panzerjäger 'Panther' für 8.8cm Pak 43/3 (Sd.Kfz.173) (als Panz.Jäg. Bef.Wg.) and outfitted in accordance with K.A.N.1154a with Fu 8 and Fu 5 radio sets in two Jagdpanther and Fu 7 and Fu 5 radio sets in the third Jagdpanther. Each schwere Panzerjäger-Kompanie 'Panther' (frei) was to be organised in accordance with K.St.N.1149a (fG) dated 1Mar44 with 14 Panzerjäger 'Panther' für 8.8cm Pak 43/3 (Sd.Kfz.173) and outfitted in accordance with K.A.N.1149a with Fu 8 and Fu 5 radio sets in the company commander's Jagdpanther, four Jagdpanther outfitted with Fu 5 and Fu 2 radio sets, and the other nine Jagdpanther with a single Fu 5 radio set. Each Jagdpanther was authorised to have one M.G.34 installed in the ball mount and one M.G.42 loose inside.

5.1 Combat Service

The first unit to obtain Jagdpanther was schwere Heeres Panzerjäger Abteilung 654. This unit had been designated for this service as early as August 1943 when they had turned the rest of their Ferdinands over to their sister unit s.H.Pz. Jag.Abt.653. The first five Jagdpanther of the production series were not completed until January 1944, and it was not until 21 February 1944 that the 654th was issued orders to reorganise into a Jagdpanther unit and commence training. Due to production delays and teething problems with the Jagdpanther, the 654th was issued five Panthers in February 1944 for driver training. On 23 March 1944, two Jagdpanther were released from the Heeres Zeugamt (ordnance depot) and sent by rail to the training grounds at Mielau for troop training. Finally the first eight Jagdpanther, issued directly to s.Pz.Jg.Abt.654, were loaded on rail cars at the Heeres Zeugamt and sent to the unit on 28 April 1944 and arrived at the train station in Rethel on 4 May 1944.

This state of combat readiness of the 654th on 6 June 1944 when the Allies landed on the Normandy beaches was that it still had only 8 Jagdpanther. On 11 June 1944, Hitler was notified that the Stab (headquarters) along with the 1. and 2. Kompanien of the 654th would be combat ready at Rethel by 18 June 1944. The Stab was to be outfitted with 3 Befehls-Panthers, the 1. Kompanie with 12 Jagdpanther, and the 2. Kompanie with 13 Jagdpanther. The 17 Jagdpanther (needed to make up the 25) were sent to the unit from the Heeres Zeugamt by rail on 14 June 1944. Due to production delays and teething problems the 654th had not been filled to its authorised establishment prior to elements of the unit being sent to the Western Front.

Completely disregarding the maxim of mass employment of new weapons or even the tactical doctrine of avoiding scattered piecemeal employment of armoured vehicles, the incomplete 2.Kompanie was ordered to be sent to the front alone. At ten minutes past midnight on 15 June 1944, the 2.Kp./ s.H.Pz.Jäg.Abt.654 with the eight available Jagdpanther loaded on rail cars started for the Western Front. Moving mostly at night, the 2.Kompanie arrived at the front on 20 June 1944 with 6 of the 8 Jagdpanther operational and subsequently was shifted around to various defensive positions. Jagdpanther broke down due to various mechanical problems during each move, resulting in only an average of 5 of the 8 Jagdpanther being operational each day.

The first combat action did not occur until 11 July 1944, when 4 Jagdpanther supported an infantry counterattack in the late afternoon. Advancing on the left flank, one Jagdpanther was penetrated by friendly fire from a Pz.Kpfw. IV belonging to the 6.Kp./Pz.Rgt.3 of the 2.Pz.Div, resulting in three of the crew being severely wounded. The remaining three Jagdpanther continued to advance carefully through close hedgerow country. One anti-tank gun and a Sherman were knocked out. While returning to the previous position, the superstructure of a Jagdpanther was penetrated by a hit from a British anti-tank gun, killing the loader and wounding the commander, gunner, and driver. By driving fast the Jagdpanther managed to pull away without getting hit again. From 12 through 17 July only two or three of the eight Jagdpanther belonging to the 2.Kompanie were operational each day.

As of 1 July 1944, the 654th reported a total strength of 25 Jagdpanther (including the 8 with the 2.Kompanie and 17 that had arrived on 19 and 20 June). The troops in the 3.Kompanie were preparing to load the 17 Jagdpanther for rail transport but did not leave for the front until 5 and 6 July 1944. An additional Jagdpanther and three Befehls-Panthers (as substitutes for three Befehls-Jagdpanther) left the Heeres-Zeugamt by rail for the 654th on 6 July 1944. The 1.Kompanie was transferred to Mailly le Camp training grounds and was still sitting there one month later without any Jagdpanther.

Finally on 17 July 1944, the Stab and the 3.Kompanie arrived at the front and were placed under the command of the XLVII.Panzer-Korps. Many breakdowns had occurred en route to the front so that the entire 654th (including the 2.Kp. and 3.Kp.) had only 8 operational Jagdpanther out of 25 on 17 July, 8 on 18 July, 10 on 19 July, 10 on 20 July, 13 on 21 July, 15 on 23 July, 17 on 24 July, 19 on 25 July, 19 on 26 July, and 20 on 27 July. On 28 July 1944, the XLVII.Panzer-Korps reported the strength of the 654th as 21 operational Jagdpanther with a further 4 undergoing repair.

Hauptmann Noak, commander of the s.H.Pz.Jg.Abt.654, wrote an experience report dated 24 July 1944 on Jagdpanther operations on the Invasion Front. In addition to a long dissertation on problems fighting in hedgerow country, this report provided extraordinary insight into the tactics forced by circumstances and the problems encountered, as follows:

After firing only two or three rounds, the Jagdpanther must change position immediately. In all cases it must drive immediately into cover and from there scout on foot for a new firing position, because when the British spot a firing position they react with artillery fire.

It is absolutely important that the Jagdpanther are camouflaged against aircraft. When possible, drive under trees with the hatches closed so that fragments from artillery shells bursting in the crowns of trees do not enter the Jagdpanther. The British always scout with aircraft and have many artillery spotters in the air. Cover the engine deck and radiator/fan louvres with boards and Panzerschürzen in assembly areas; otherwise damage will often occur to the radiators from shell fragments.

Every advance or leap from firing position to firing position must be scouted on foot because frequently there is a deep sunken path behind an easily driven-through hedgerow. Every unnecessary movement should be avoided; otherwise artillery fire occurs immediately. Do not make long position changes in the main battle zone at night; wait until dawn or dusk, because noise can be heard a long way at night and there is more heavy artillery fire at night than during the day or evening.

At close or medium range do not aim at enemy tanks with the Ziel aufsitzend (point of inverted V at the base of the target); instead use Zielmitte because when the superstructure or turret is penetrated the tank easily burns. By Ziel aufsitzend more shots hit lower in the hull, resulting in the crews bailing out, but the tank does not start to burn.

When an attack is recognised, drive into the scouted firing positions, because it is easier to catch the opponent in the open than to throw them out of a defensive position. During enemy tank attacks (usually with 3 or 4 tanks) let them close to short range and when possible knock out the last tank first, or otherwise usually the rest will disappear using smoke.

Use the Fu 5 and even the Fu 8 only in extreme emergencies, because the British quickly intercept the signals and reply with artillery fire. Mostly one can send commands only by messenger and flag signals. It is absolutely necessary that the battle plan be discussed in detail in advance with the Jagdpanther commanders and escorted infantry.

During the approximately 300-kilometre march from the unloading train stations to the front, the following mechanical failures occurred in the 25 Jagdpanther: 18 final drives, 2 HL 230 engines, 3 oil coolers, 3 fan drives, 2 idlers, 1 idler crank arm, 1 torsion bar, 4 road wheels, 4 drive sprockets, and 1 main drive shaft as well as wearing out 109 track links. The following parts were damaged in action: 1 transmission, 4 radiators, 1 oil cooler, 4 fan drives, 6 drive sprockets, 2 final drives, and 16 road wheels.

Modification of the rear deck louvres for cooling air is urgently requested to prevent shell fragments from above entering! This is the same long-standing request from the troops for S-form or angled louvres on air intakes. All radiator damage has been caused by shell fragments from above. The electrical system is not properly suppressed, because interference caused by highly revved engines and steering makes it impossible for the crew to hear on the intercom or radio. The forward right periscope on the superstructure and the closed commander's

Above: In France, a damaged Jagdpanther of Pz.Jg.Abt.654 is towed by second Jagdpanther (ADO)
Below: Jagdpanther in the 1.Kp/s.Pz.Jg.Abt.654 were modified by the unit. Most tool stowage was relocated to the rear and self-fabricated stowage bins were mounted on the superstructure rear. (KHM)

hatch are not watertight, so that rainwater shorts out the radio sets. The 2m Stabantennen (aerial) break off by minimal contact with branches, because the springs in the Antennenfuss 2 are too strong.

By 30 July 1944, the 654th had been transferred to the LXXIV.Armee-Korps, which reported that the 654th had destroyed 10 enemy tanks out of 25 knocked out in their sector. In a two-minute action on 30 July, three Jagdpanther engaged a squadron of Churchills from the 6th Guards Tank Brigade. Two additional Churchill squadrons joined the action, forcing the Jagdpanther to retire behind the crest of a hill after the Jagdpanther had received some hits. The 6th Guards Tank Brigade reported the loss of 11 Churchills in this short action and claimed to have found 2 Jagdpanther abandoned on the reverse slope of the ridge with some track damage.

The first total loss of a Jagdpanther (tactical number 311, Fgst.Nr.300014) occurred on 31 July when it was blown up by its crew to prevent it from falling into enemy hands. Disabled by mechanical failure of a final drive, the Jagdpanther had been spotted by the enemy, was under heavy artillery fire, cut off by enemy infantry, and there was no tank retriever available.

On 1 August 1944, the 654th reported being down to 8 operational Jagdpanther and 2 operational Befehls-Panthers, with a further 16 Jagdpanther requiring repair. One Jagdpanther and one Befehls-Panther had been lost in action during July, and another two Jagdpanther were written off on 1 August. The unit strength during the first half of August was reduced from a high of 12 operational Jagdpanther on the 2nd, down to 6 on the 3rd, 4 on the 4th, 3 on the 5th, 7 on the 6th, 5 on the 7th, 4 on the 8th, 3 on the 9th, 3 on the 10th, 3 on the 11th, 2 on the 12th and only 1 on the 13th.

Meanwhile, in order to finally fill the 654th to its complete authorised establishment of 14 in each of the three companies, 16 additional Jagdpanther were issued to the unit in July. Eight were sent by rail from the Heeres Zeugamt on 31 July and the last eight on 14 August 1944. Even though it only possessed 8 Jagdpanther that had arrived in Mailly le Camp on 3 August, the 1.Kp./s.H.Pz.Jäg.Abt.654 was declared to be combat ready and sent to the front, loading on trains on 7 August and unloading on 9 August at Chalons. Continuing by road march through Paris it reached the front on 16 August. Caught up in the general retreat and never really getting into action the 1.Kp. finally joined up with the rest of the 654th on 28 August. The last 8 Jagdpanther were also sent to the front and joined the 654th on 29 August, having lost one en route.

During a period of continuous withdrawals to prevent being trapped in the Falaise pocket and southwest of the Seine River, the 654th lost a total of 19 Jagdpanther in

A Jagdpanther Ausf.G1 with the s.Pz. Jg.Abt.654, issued to the unit in October 1944, had a single driver's periscope with a thin plate welded over the second hole at the assembly plant. (KHM)

August (15 during the retreat). The 654th successfully retired across the Seine River with 23 surviving Jagdpanther most of which needed major repairs.

A Jagdpanther (tactical number 314, Fgst.Nr.300027 lost on 1 August 1944) was reported to be captured by the British in mid-August. A battalion of the British 43rd Division claimed the credit for stopping the Jagdpanther by a round fired from a 6-pounder anti-tank gun which jammed the left sprocket. A hollow-charge round fired from a PIAT had penetrated the right superstructure side, but it did not do any appreciable damage. The superstructure roof had also been perforated, probably by a high-explosive round. Recovery of this Jagdpanther for shipment back to England for research and testing was undertaken. An attempt to winch the Jagdpanther onto a Diamond-T tank trailer was aborted when the Jagdpanther buried its head in a ditch, pitched the trailer high into the air, and at the same time smashed the winch of a Scammell attempting to hold it in position. The 43rd Division Royal Engineers wagered 1000 francs that the Jagdpanther weighed more than the reported 46 tons.

Ordered to pull out on 9 September 1944, the 654th was sent to rest and refit in the Grafenwöhr training area in Bavaria. To repair their Jagdpanther, the 654th requested 7 Maybach HL230 engines, 5 AK 7-200 transmissions, 23 complete sets of track, and 23 drive sprockets. They reported that the normal Panther final drive gears and even the strengthened final drive gears were quickly failing due to the extra weight and nose-heavy Jagdpanther. The normal Panther final drive gears were lasting an average of only 35 kilometres before failure of an inner gear shaft. By 28 October, the final drive problem had apparently been solved when the 654th reported that Jagdpanther with strengthened final drives had driven 400 to 500 kilometres without any failures. However, it was noticed that the drive sprockets were severely stressed.

Urgently needed to shore up the defence in the West, the 654th was rebuilt to the complete authorised strength of 45 Jagdpanther through receipt of 9 on 14 October, 7 on 23 October, and the last 6 on 15 November 1944. In addition to the Jagdpanther, the 654th had received four 2cm Fla-Vierling auf Panzer IV and four 3.7cm Flak auf Panzer IV to outfit a Panzer Flazug for mobile anti-aircraft defence. It also had four Bergepanthers to outfit the Bergestaffel for recovery and repair of broken-down or damaged Jagdpanther. The 654th was loaded on trains at Grafenwöhr and started back to the Western Front on 18 November. On the way to the front, the axles overheated on a SSY-Wagen (super-heavy railcar) carrying two Jagdpanther which apparently never caught up with their unit until December. Attached to

As reported by the commander of s.Pz.Jg.Abt.654, Hauptmann Noak, "The frontal armour of the Jagdpanther is no longer sufficient in the West because even the glacis plate has been frequently penetrated by enemy tank and anti-tank fire at medium range (200 to 500 metres)." (NARA)

the LXIII.Armee-Korps in A.O.K.19 of Heeres Gruppe G, the 654th was continuously in action from 20 through 30 November 1944. During this period the 654th claimed to have destroyed 52 enemy tanks and 10 enemy anti-tank guns and to have damaged an additional 9 enemy tanks. Their own reported total losses were 18 Jagdpanther and three 2cm Fla-Vierling auf Panzer IV. As of 1 December 1944, the 1.Kompanie had 10 Jagdpanther, the 2. Kompanie had 7 Jagdpanther, and the 3.Kompanie had 8 Jagdpanther - all in operational condition.

As recorded in the experience report from Hauptmann Noak, commander of s.Pz.Jg.Abt.654 on 11 December 1944:

During the period from 20 November to 11 December 1944, the Abteilung lost 20 Jagdpanther (total write-offs) and had achieved the following success: 65 enemy tanks and 2 armoured cars destroyed, 11 enemy tanks and 2 armoured cars disabled though hits, and 15 enemy anti-tank guns, 1 armoured half-track, 1 towing vehicle, 3 trucks, 2 cars, and several infantry units destroyed.

The frontal armour of the Jagdpanther is no longer sufficient in the West because even the front sloping glacis plate has been frequently penetrated by enemy tank and anti-tank fire at medium range (200 to 500 metres).

Most of the Jagdpanther losses are not caused by enemy tanks or anti-tank guns. In general they are lost because tracks and final drives are damaged by artillery, and when our own infantry must pull back under the pressure of the numerically superior enemy, the Jagdpanther can no longer be retrieved and must be blown up.

In general the Jagdpanther has proven to be good. When the enemy discovers Jagdpanther during his attacks they mostly try to pull away and restart their attack in another position.

Due to the numerous delays in production, the 654th was the only unit that had all three companies completely outfitted with Jagdpanther. To compensate for this production shortage, on 11 September 1944, Hitler ordered that a trial organisation be established consisting of a mixture of Jagdpanther and Jagdpanzer IV or Sturmgeschütz. Each Abteilung was to consist of one Jagdpanther company and two companies of Jagdpanzer IV or Sturmgeschütz III. Hitler specifically stated that he did not want additional Jagdpanther Abteilungen completely outfitted with 45 Jagdpanther. The trial organisation was to be immediately implemented with s.H.Pz.Jäg.Abt.559 at the troop training area in Mielau. The next unit ordered to implement this change was s.H.Pz.Jäg.Abt.525, which was still employed with its Hornissen in Italy.

As with many other recorded orders and directives noted in Hitler's conferences, this organisational change had already taken place before Hitler was informed. The 559th had already been ordered to change to this new organisation in August 1944, and the 525th was never completely pulled out of Italy to convert to Jagdpanther.

Having lost their last seven 7.5cm Pak 40 Sfl. auf Pz.38(t) on the Eastern Front by 10 February 1944, the 559th received orders on 21 February to return to the Mielau Panzer Jäger training centre and arrived on 28 February. Two Jagdpanther were available for training at Mielau in March and the unit was issued their first five Jagdpanther, which were sent by rail from the Heeres Zeugamt on 18 May 1944. A long dry spell followed, with no additional combat vehicle being issued until 28 Sturmgeschütz III and 11 Jagdpanther were shipped by rail between 21 and 25 August 1944. The last 2 Jagdpanther for the 559th were not loaded and sent from the Heeres Zeugamt until 3 September 1944, directly after the 559th had been loaded on rail cars and sent to the Western Front. Having left Mielau on 1 September, the 559th had unloaded at Utrecht and was available for action by 6 September 1944. It was not unusual at this time for a unit to be shipped out directly after receiving their contingent of armoured vehicles with very little time allowed for individual crew familiarisation let alone tactical training involving an entire company or the whole Abteilung.

Problems encountered in the tactical employment of the Jagdpanther are revealed in the following experience report dated 28 September 1944 from an Oberleutnant who was the commander of s.Pz.Jg.Abt.559 (Panther):

Due to the attachment situation, only one Sturmgeschütz-Kompanie was employed during attacks on the Böringen bridgehead, where strong enemy tank forces had been expected as reported by reconnaissance troops and infantry. When it was revealed during the battle that in comparison to the enemy tanks the Sturmgeschütz were outnumbered and could not break through in every zone, the Panther-Kompanie was also sent in. This piecemeal employment led to our heavy losses. The Abteilung is convinced that a concentrated attack by a combined force of Sturmgeschütz and Jagdpanther would have resulted in the destruction of all of the enemy tanks found there, cleaned out the bridgehead, and our own losses would have been significantly lower.

Even though the Panzerjäger-Kompanien were subordinate to the Infanterie-Regiments, the attack was directed by the Kompanien. The grounds for this were: (a) command of a Kompanie by radio on a broad strip is easier than directing infantry units, and (b) the infantry stuck very closely to the armoured vehicles and out of necessity followed their every movement.

Therefore leading the attack should be given to the commander of the armoured units or the infantry commander should work closely with the armoured commander, utilizing the radios to direct all the armoured vehicles and his infantry. However, correct employment of the armoured force must be the highest priority.

In previous battles there were always large problems in freeing the armoured forces from the infantry in order to engage other enemy concentrations. The infantry commander strong concern for his unit's security results in him always holding the armoured force back even if they are not employed at the correct location (Schwerpunkt). Since this is backed by the higher command, it leads to scattering our armoured force, with the result that success is not achieved and our own losses are unnecessarily high.

Attempts by the Abteilung to pull the Sturmgeschütz and Jagdpanther out of the Kampfzone after every action in order to create a central mobile reserve in readiness behind the supported sector also did not succeed. This situation led to the Panzers being in direct action for so long that they were either totally lost or small mechanical problems left unattended degraded to where major repairs were needed in the Werkstatt and fell out for a longer period.

As an example the Panther-Kompanie, which must absolutely be serviced after driving 250 kilometres, drove a stretch of over 600 kilometres without any maintenance halts. Sufficient examples have occurred as to how detrimental this can be on the vehicles, resulting in decreased unit combat capability.

Therefore, the Abteilung encourages:

1. *Concentrated employment of the entire Abteilung under the direction of its own commander.*
2. *Subordination of infantry units in the Abteilung sector or close coordination with them.*
3. *Actions of the schwere Panzer-Jäger and infantry must be aligned with the tactics of the Panzerjäger and not the reverse. The entire operation must be built based on this principle.*
4. *After every action, immediately pull the Panzerjägers out and create a mobile reserve behind the assigned sector."*

By 29 September, the 559th, down to 9 Jagdpanther (of which 3 were operational) and 8 Sturmgeschütz (all requiring repair), was transferred to the LXVIII.Armee-Korps in A.O.K.15 under Heeres Gruppe B. On 4 October, the 559th was in possession of 3 operational Jagdpanther and 5 operational Sturmgeschütz and had been promised an additional issue of 12 Sturmgeschütz III. Having been in continuous action, the 559th was still at the front on 1 November and reported that they were down to 6 Jagdpanther in the 3.Kompanie (only 1 operational) plus 15 Sturmgeschütz III (of which 3 were operational).

The third unit to see action with Jagdpanther, schwere Heeres Panzerjäger-Abteilung 519, had been decimated on the Eastern Front in the Heeres Gruppe Mitte sector, having lost the last of their Hornissen in June and July 1944. Transferred back to Mielau for rebuilding by August 1944, the 519th was ordered to reorganise on 22 August 1944 as follows:

- Jagdpanther-Abt.Stab (K.St.N.1106 v.1.3.44)
- Stabskp. (K.St.N.1154a v.1.3.44)
- 1.Pz.Jg.'Panther' Kp. (K.St.N.1149 v. 1.4.44)
- 2.Pz.Jg.Sturmgeschütz Kp. (K.St.N.1149 v. 1.4.44)
- 3.Pz.Jg.Sturmgeschütz Kp. (K.St.N.1149 v. 1.4.44)

A total of 17 Jagdpanther and 28 Sturmgeschütz III. The 28 Sturmgeschütz III were sent by rail from the Heeres Zeugamt on 6 September, and the 17 Jagdpanther were sent between 14 and 27 September 1944.

Loaded on rail cars in six trains, the 519th left Mielau for the Western Front during the morning of 8 October, and the last of the trains arrived and was unloaded on 11 October 1944. Under Heeres Gruppe G, tactically assigned to the LXXXI.Armee-Korps, the 519th reported the following operational status for their Jagdpanther:

Date	Strength	Operational	Losses
22Oct	17	11	0
27Oct	17	6	0
29Oct	14	5	3
31Oct	14	7	0
1Nov	14	10	0
4Nov	14	12	0
24Nov	11	4	3
28Nov	10	1	1
1Dec	10	2	0
6Dec	9	4	1
10Dec	9	1	0
11Dec	9	4	0
15Dec	9	4	0

The average strength of 9 operational Jagdpanther in October had been reduced to 7 in November, and sank to an average of 3 operational Jagdpanther during the first half of December. While most units were issued sufficient armoured vehicles to fill them to the authorised organisation strength before they were sent to the front, continuous action quickly whittled units down to only a small fraction of their intended combat effectiveness.

To support the upcoming offensives on the Western Front, the OKH planned to have five schwere Heeres Panzer-Jäger-Abteilungen outfitted with Jagdpanther to be available with Heeres Gruppe B and G in December 1944. Of these five units, three (654th, 559th, and 519th) were already at the front and were no longer at full strength. Two additional units, the 560th and 655th, had been recently outfitting at the Panzerjäger training centre in Mielau.

The 560th, sitting at Mielau waiting for equipment since April 1944, was sent 4 Jagdpanther from the Heeres Zeugamt on 8 October, 4 on 22 November, 1 on 30 November, and 4 on 6 December. Instead of Sturmgeschütz IIIs or Befehls-Jagdpanther, the Abteilung Stab and two companies were issued 31 Panzer IV/70(V), which were sent to the 560th between 6 October and 2 December 1944. The 560th was loaded on railcars and left for the Western Front on 3 December, arrived, and unloaded in the Rommerskirchen Niederhausen area on 8 December 1944.

The last unit to be prepared for the Western Front offensives, the 655th had returned to Mielau by August 1944, having left their 3.Kompanie behind on the Eastern Front. Five Jagdpanther were sent to the 2.Kompanie on 24 November, but the last nine Jagdpanther were not sent from the Heeres Zeugamt until 24 December - too late for this company to take part in the offensives in December. Again, instead of Sturmgeschütz IIIs, 28 Panzer IV/70(V) were sent to the 655th for two companies on 25 November and three Panzer IV/70(V) were sent to the Abteilung Stab on 7 December. Leaving the Jagdpanther-Kompanie behind, the 31 Panzer IV/70(V) were loaded on railcars in early December, arrived and unloaded in Munchen Gladbach on 9 December 1944.

The status of the Jagdpanther on the Western Front on the morning of 16 December 1944 at the time of the start of the Ardennes offensive was 5 with the 559th under Pz.Lehr-Div., 9 with the 519th in the 6.Pz.Armee, and 13 with the 560th under the 12.SSPz.Div. The 8 replacements sent to the 559th on 13 December and 4 sent to the 519th on 15 December did not arrive at the front for the units until early January. S.Pz.Jg.Abt.654 with 26 Jagdpanther further south under H.Gr.Oberhein received 10 replacements by 25 December and another 9 on 5 January. Jagdpanther for the fifth unit, s.Pz.Jg.Abt. 560 under the 10.SS-Pz.Div., did not reach the front until after 15 January 1945.

Of the total planned strength of 56 Jagdpanther for Heeres Gruppe B, only 27 were available at the start of the Ardennes offensive. Of these approximately 17 (not more than 20) were operational when Heeres Gruppe B started to attack on 16 December. The three Abteilungen that took part in the offensive had total losses of 5 Jagdpanther plus additional temporary loses due to damage in combat and mechanical failures. As of 30 December 1944, there were 4 Jagdpanther (2 operational and one total loss) with the 559th and 9 Jagdpanther (4 operational and no total loss) with the 519th. No report was available from the 560th for the end of the year. However the 560th operating under the 12th SS Pz.Div. were in heavy fighting and back-calculating from later reports must have lost 4 Jagdpanther in December. The 654th employed much farther to the south under Heeres Gruppe G reported 28 operational Jagdpanther and 7 in repair on 30 December 1944.

Additional Jagdpanther were sent to the Western Front as replacements from the Heereszeugamt, with the 560th being sent 2 on 11 January, the 559th sent 6 on 13 January, and the 519th sent 6 on 14 January. A strength report from the West dated 5 February 1945 reveals a high operational percentage and relatively low losses during January, as follows:

Unit	Jagdpanther	Operational	Losses
654	41	26	3
519	11	9	8
560	6	3	5
655	14	12	0
559	18	?	0

A further 30 Jagdpanther were issued to units in the West in January 1945. Ten were shipped to the 654th on 25 January, 10 to the 560th on 29 January, and 10 to the 655th on 29 January. But none of these Jagdpanther had arrived at the units until after the above report dated 5 February 1945.

All through 1944 not a single Jagdpanther had been issued to units sent to the Eastern Front. Finally on 13 January 1945, 10 Jagdpanther were sent to units (5 for s.H.Pz.Jg.Abt.563 and 5 for the 1.Kp./s.H.Pz.Jäg.Abt.616) intended for the Eastern Front. These 10 were diverted in transit and did not reach the intended units. A further nine were sent from the Heereszeugamt on 15 January, followed by another nine Jagdpanther the next day.

As reported by the unit commander on 2 February 1945: The schwere Heeres Panzerjäger-Abteilung 563 had returned from Kurland to the Mielau training grounds on 3 December 1944. There they received orders to outfit one company with Jagdpanther and two companies with Panzer IV/70 (V). Having completed their basic training for the three companies, the 653rd was sent into action as infantry on 17 January and lost 55 men, including many skilled commanders, gunners, and drivers. First sent to Soldau to pick up the Jagdpanzers, the 563rd was then sent to Allenstein, where they finally received their armoured vehicles on 20 January. One company had 9 Jagdpanther and the other two companies each received 12 Panzer IV/70(V). The unit strength was increased by attaching a fourth company, the 3.Kp./s.H.Pz.Jg.Abt.616, which also had 9 Jagdpanther. Outfitting, training, and general familiarity with the Jagdpanzers were accomplished in record time, starting at 1000 hours on 20 January and ending at 0700 hours on 21 January. That same day the 563rd was sent into combat north of Allenstein. In late January, the 563rd assisted in retaking Leibstadt, and they finished the month in the Wormditt area. During 10 days in action the 563rd claimed to have destroyed 58 enemy tanks. Their own losses due to direct enemy action were one Jagdpanther and four Panzer IV/70(V) totally destroyed. Circumstances forced the 563rd to destroy the following additional Jagdpanzers by setting off internal charges as follows: 8 Jagdpanther and 4 Panzer IV/70(V) due to fuel shortages, 1 Jagdpanther and 8 Panzer IV/70(V) that were stuck in mud and ice, and 3 Jagdpanther and 5 Panzer IV/70(V) due to a shortage of repair parts. Indirect causes instead of direct enemy action had decimated the 563rd, leaving the unit with only 5 Jagdpanther and 3 Panzer IV/70 (V) on 1 February 1945.

Month	No.	Sent	Unit	Front
Jan45	14	22Jan	I.Abt./Pz.Rgt.29	East
Feb45	14	10Feb	I.Abt/Pz.Rgt.130	West
	10	14Feb	2.SS Pz.Div.	East
	8	14Feb	4.Pz.Div.	East
	10	14Feb	9.SS Pz.Div.	East
	10	15Feb	Führ.Gr.Div.	West
	6	24Feb	s.Pz.Jg.Abt.654	West
	10	28Feb	10.SS Pz.Div.	East
Mar45	5	13Mar	s.Pz.Jg.Abt.559	West
	15	27Mar	116.Pz.Div.	West
	4	30Mar	25.Pz.Div.	East
Apr45	35	7Apr	II.Abt/Pz.Rgt.130	West
	10	8Apr	s.Pz.Jg.Abt.655	West
	10	17Apr	s.Pz.Jg.Abt.519	West
	9	21Apr	s.Pz.Jg.Abt.519	West

Starting in January 1945, in addition to supplying replacements to already established s.H.Pz.Jg.Abt., Jagdpanther were now being issued to Panzer-Regiments and to Panzerjäger-Abteilungen that were organic to Panzer-Divisions. As ordered on 21 January, the I.Abt./Pz.Rgt.29 was to have one Kompanie of 14 Jagdpanther organised in accordance with K.St.N.1149(f.G.) dated 1Apr44.

The 6 Jagdpanther sent to s.Pz.Jg.Abt.654 on 24 February arrived on 7 March and were issued to the 4.Kompanie (formerly the 1.Kp./Pz.Jg.Abt.525). As a demonstration of the turmoil, frustration, and counterorders occurring at this time, the 10 Jagdpanther that were finally received by the 10.SS-Panzer-Division in late March had first been ordered on 28 February to be issued to the 7. Panzer-Division and then on 3 March to Panzer-Division 'Holstein'. On 9 March 1945, Panzer-Brigade 103 was ordered to be disbanded, with the remaining 6 Jagdpanther from I.Abt./Pz.Rgt.29 to be given to the 8.Pz.Div.

The 35 Jagdpanther issued to the 2.Panzer-Division under Heeres Gruppe G near Schweinfurt had initially been issued to the II.Abt./Pz.Rgt.130 of the Pz.Lehr Div and were reported as having been taken over by Stab Reick.

The highest number of Jagdpanther in service at the front was reported on 15 March 1945 as:

Eastern Front

Unit	Operational	Repair	Issued
Pz.Div.Holstein	0	0	10
10.SS Pz.Div.	1	5	
9.SS Pz.Div.	6	4	
Führer Gren.Div.	2	5	
2.SS Pz.Div.	10	0	
s.Pz.Jg.Abt.560	7	6	
8.Pz.Div.	2	4	
25.Pz.Div.	0	0	4
4.Pz.Div.	3	0	
1./Pz.Jg.Abt.563	3	4	

Western Front

Unit	Operational	Repair	Issued
s.Pz.Jg.Abt.655	4	7	
s.Pz.Jg.Abt.654	12	27	
s.Pz.Jg.Abt.559	2	7	5
Pz.Lehr-Div.	5	7	35
s.Pz.Jg.Abt.519	2	10	

The last available strength report dated 10 April 1945 reveals how badly the situation had deteriorated one month prior to the end of the war (top of next page).

Eastern Front

Unit	Operational	In Repair
8.Pz.Div.	2	2
10.SS Pz.Div.	3	3
25.Pz.Div.	2	4
Führer Gren.Div.	2	3
2.SS Pz.Div.	2	0

Western Front

Unit	Operational	In Repair
Pz.Lehr-Div.	0	1
s.Pz.Jg.Abt.654	5	24
s.Pz.Jg.Abt.519	0	0

Not all of the units that possessed Jagdpanther on 10 April 1945 did or could report. This report shows a grand total of only 16 operational Jagdpanther, but there were at least an additional 71 Jagdpanther not shown in the above report which were picked up by units in April 1945, as follows:

1Apr45. *7 Jagdpanther in Wunsdorf and 4 Jagdpanther in Braunschweig from March production are immediately available for issue and planned to be issued to H.Pz.Jg.Abt.560.*
5Apr45 As a change to the order dated 3Apr45, s.Pz.Jg.Abt.559 under H.Gr.H is to receive 12 Jagdpanther sent to Pz.Stutzpunkt Nord.
5Apr45. *s.Pz.Jg.Abt.519 is to be transferred by H.Gr.G to the Weissenfels area and there issued Jagdpanther from Pz.-Zeugamt Braunschweig.*
5Apr45. *s.Pz.Jg.Abt.655 under Pz.A.O.K.1 with 90% of its vehicles requiring lengthy repairs was pulled out for maintenance to the area northeast of Suhlingen with 7 Jagdpz.IV L/70 in the 1.Kp., 8 Jagdpanther in the 2.Kp., 5 Jagdpz.IV L/70 in the 3.Kp., 3 Fla-Pz.IV (2cm Vierling) and 3 Fla-Pz.IV (3.7cm) in the Pz-Fla-Zug, and 1 Bergepanther in the Werkst.Zug.*
5Apr45. *The 35 operational Jagdpanther along with the crews that are available in the Braunschweig area are to be sent to Schweinfurt to fill the 2.Pz.Div.*
6Apr45. *s.H.Pz.Jg.Abt.519 is to be sent to the 2.Pz.Div. area and on orders from OKW to receive in the area of Schweinfurt-Bamberg the 35 Jagdpanther being sent from Braunschweig. At present, s.Pz.Jg.Abt.519 is not to be issued any Jagdpanther.*
6Apr45. *Oberschrim. Ziegler from H.Za. Braunschweig reported at 1730 hours: 35 Jagdpanther for the 2.Pz.Div. are completely ready with train and transport numbers assigned. 35 Ssyms-Wagen, 12 GWagen, and 4 M-Wagen and Schutzwagen are needed. Major Ditzer was informed at 1745 hours to do everything to acquire these railcars immediately. There are still 2 Jagdpanther in H.Za. Braunschweig and an additional 6 are to be completed by 8 April. Issue to? There are 9 operational Jagdpanther available at M.N.H., Hannover-Laatzen. These Jagdpanther must be driven by road since rail transport is not possible. Fuel is not available. Issue to?*
7Apr45. *Hitler has assigned s.H.Pz.Jg.Abt.655 as Heerestruppe for A.O.K.12. 12 Jagdpanther are underway to them from Braunschweig.*
10Apr45. *Oberstlt. Rudolph in Braunschweig called at 0245 hours: On 9 April 1945 at 0730 hours 10 Jagdpanther and 1 Bergepanther with full crews, ammunition, and fuel left for Soltau by rail for s.Pz.Jg.Abt.655.*

Hauptmann Köppen, sent to M.N.H. Hannover on 7 April 1945, was ordered: All of the Panther hulls in M.N.H. that were moved out by 8 April are to be sent to Braunschweig. In total, 2 Jagdpanther (complete, without guns) and 1 Jagdpanther (with damaged engine) were sent to Wefensleben near Helmstedt. There are two possibilities: use these as Bergefahrzeuge for II./Pz.Rgt.130 or load on railcars in Helmstedt and send to Altengrabow. Decision requested.

At M.I.A.G. in Braunschweig there is one Versuchs-Jagdpanther available as well as two partially completed Jagdpanther with engines, transmission, and final drives but missing swing arms, roadwheels, and tracks. It is proposed that these be made mobile and transported to Altengrabow. The Versuchs-Jagdpanther that is finished today is to be given to s.Pz.Jg.Abt.655.

In addition three complete Jagdpanther hulls with guns and three without guns are available. The order given on 7 April 1945 to disable the M.I.A.G. assembly plant was rescinded on 9 April. M.I.A.G. intends to start on 10 April to complete these 6 Jagdpanther. Crews for them are secured. Whether this attempt succeeds depends on the enemy situation. Decision needed.

10Apr45. *Plans are to deliver 11 Jagdpanther to s.H.Pz.Jg.Abt.560 after 15Apr.*
15Apr45. *The 11 Jagdpanther at M.B.A. Drewitz, Potsdam are to be taken over by Pz.Jg.Abt.559. These 11 Jagdpanther and 1 Bergepanther previously issued to the 560th on 10 April are to be given to the 559th.*
19Apr45. *20 Jagdpanther with Pz.Jg.Abt.559 are to be assigned to the 7.Pz.Div. The 2.Kp./Pz.Jg.Abt.559 received 2 Jagdpanther in Döberitz and are to receive a further 7 in about 3 to 4 days. Jagdpanther assembly situation for s.Pz.Jg.Abt.559 at M.B.A. Drewitz is: 1 Jagdpanther completed on 18Apr, 1 Jagdpanther to be completed the evening of 19Apr, and 7 Jagdpanther planned to be completed in 3 days. Guns are not presently available at M.B.A. for 14 Jagdpanther which are to be sent by truck.*
20Apr45. *4 Jagdpanther have been completed by M.B.A.-Drewitz, and another 5 are to be completed by 22 April for a total of 9.*

20Apr45. *s.H.Pz.Jg.Abt.559 with Stabskp. one Kompanie, and a Werkstattzug is attached to the 7.Pz.Div. The Abteilung has already arrived at the division and reported having 19 Jagdpanther.*
26Apr45. *s.H.Pz.Jg.Abt.559 with 16 Jagdpanther (12 operational) attached to the 7.Pz.Div.*
28Apr45. *Pz.Abt.106 (F.H.H.) with 3 Pz.V and 4 Jagdpanther is attached to Pz.Gren.Div. 'Clausewitz'.*

The well-known author of many books on German armour, Walter J. Spielberger, was an officer in a unit that had been ordered to be outfitted with Jagdpanzer 38. According to his contemporary account, his unit went to Hanover on 7 April and without authorisation from the OKH picked up 7 Jagdpanther at the M.N.H. assembly plant directly before it was captured by the Allies on 9 April. Attached to Panzer Gruppe Lechs, a splinter group that had been sent back to Germany to refit, the unit was continuously forced to retire and lost the majority of the Jagdpanther through lack of fuel and breakdowns.

Some of the problems encountered in employing Jagdpanther toward the end of the war were revealed by Oberlt. Bock in his trip report for 8-10 April 1945, as follows:

I had the assignment to gather the situation reports from the Panzer-Divisions in the 6.Pz. and 8.Armee and determine why during the retreat in Hungary an unusually high number of Jagdpanzers were blown up by the s.H.Pz.Jg.Abt.560. Discussions with the commander of s.H.Pz.Jg.Abt.560 revealed:

The Abteilung was attached to the 12.SS-Pz.Div. and employed as a third battalion in the Panzer-Regiment. The Abteilung's supply company was combined into a supply group with the supply units from Panzer-Regiment. The recovery service for the Abteilung was also incorporated into the Regiment in order to have a central command for recovery and maintenance. Therefore any influence over supply and repair was taken away from the Abteilung commander. In addition, the Ordannanz-Offz. was commandeered to the Regiment, so that no one was available within the Abteilung to look after these things.

The Abteilung was not issued any fuel during the retreat from Bakony Wald to Ödendurg. The 9 Jagdpanzer IV and 3 Panzerjäger V that are still available could be saved only by taking fuel from other units.

That most Panzers were blown up can be blamed on the lack of organisation in recovery that should have been accomplished by the Regiment. Recovery of the Regiment's vehicles always received priority while recovery of the 560th Jagdpanzers was always shoved back to the last.

In most cases it was then too late to conduct recovery, because our own infantry were not preventing the Russians from overrunning the location of the immobilised Jagdpanzers, regardless of whether they were only stuck or had minor automotive damage. As an example, the first recovery attempt was made on 21 March for a Jagdpanzer that became stuck on 8 March.

In most cases the continuous demands and urgent requests by the Abteilung commander to the Regiment and Division for recovery services did not achieve any results, or the reply was that recovery services were not available and in an emergency the vehicles should be blown up. The Panzer-Regiment had total command over the Jagdpanzers and distributed the repair of Jagdpanzers to any unit without informing the Abteilung, so that the Abteilung commander never had a picture of how many operational Jagdpanzers were currently available or where elements were located.

An additional cause for loss of numerous Jagdpanzers was due to tactically incorrect employment. Almost without exception, the Jagdpanzers were employed as Sturmgeschütz in most cases left with infantry as a rearguard in contact with the enemy. For a vehicle that can only fire to the front, this is disadvantageous since it must turn around to take up a firing position. In several cases it was ordered to dig-in damaged Jagdpanzers, which is an impossible task for a vehicle that can only fire to the front. The result was loss of the Jagdpanzer, which had to be blown up to prevent it from falling into enemy hands.

Due to the fact that the Panzer-Regiment had complete control of the tactical employment, as well as the supply, recovery, and repair, there cannot be any talk about the Abteilung commander being responsible. In practice, the Abteilung commander was only a company commander within the Panzer-Regiment.

The relative value placed on the Jagdpanther is revealed in a report from the Chef des Stabes of the General Inspektor der Panzertruppen dated 14 March 1945 on development questions: It is the opinion of the Gen.Insp.d.Pz.Tr. that when the emergency program goes into effect, even when they are the most modern and reliable design, 75 'Panther' 8.8cm are in no way more valuable than 150 Pz.IV lang (V) even with all this Jagdpanzer weaknesses. However, Jagdpanther are demanded instead of the Pz.IV lang (V). The number that can actually be produced is dependent on the steel allotment. Since the 'Panther' 8.8cm will not get into production until the end of 1945, in order to obtain armoured vehicles with an 8.8cm gun in the interim, the Jagdpanther should continue being produced at a rate of 150 per month until it can be replaced by 150 'Panther' 8.8cm per month.

This Befehls-Jagdpanther of 8./Pz.Lehr-Rgt.130 was lost on the Dollbergen to Uetze road on the 10 April 1945. It is a M.I.A.G. assembled Ausf.G2 that has been fitted with the Motor Abdeckung shields over the air intakes and outlets. (DB)

Above: A M.I.A.G assembled Jagdpanther Ausf.G2 that has been fitted with the Motor Abdeckung shields over the air intakes and outlets. (LA)
Below: This M.I.A.G assembled Jagdpanther Ausf.G2 was abandoned on 7 May 1945. The details of the Motor Abdeckung shields over the air intakes can be clearly seen. The cover over the outlet and crew heater could be folded back when required. (LA)